CW00664147

introduction

ANNE MCCAFFREY

lettering

TOM ORZECHOWSKI

logo designers

HARALD GRAHAM
& MARK COX

collection editor

LYNN ADAIR

collection designer

JULIE GASSAWAY

collection design manager

BRIAN GOGOLIN

publisher

MIKE RICHARDSON

This book collects issues one through six of the Marvel comic-book series The Black Dragon™ *originally edited by Jo Duffy, Archie Goodwin, and Jim Shooter.*

Published by Titan Books
42-44 Dolben St
London SE 1 OUP

May 1996
First UK edition
ISBN: 1-85286-620-9

10 9 8 7 6 5 4 3 2 1
Printed in Canada

story

CHRIS CLAREMONT

art

JOHN BOLTON

TITAN BOOKS

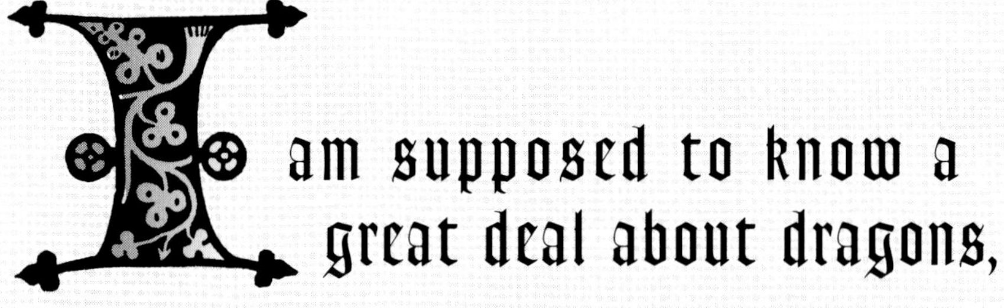
I am supposed to know a
great deal about dragons,

which, frankly, I don't. I made mine up, you see, and get a lot more credit than I deserve.

However, I do enjoy reading what other people do to dragons — now that I have such a vested interest in the creatures.

Therefore, I approached Chris Claremont's *Black Dragon* with considerable professional interest. Having John Bolton do all the illustrations was a great boon as John has obviously spent a good deal of time getting the anatomy of horses right and researching weaponry and medieval times. Such attention to detail improves the whole feeling of the story.

Set in 1193, shortly after the death of King Henry and before Richard the Lionhearted returned to England, the yarn includes such marvelous characters as Eleanor of Aquitaine and the attainted Earl of Huntingdon, aka Robin Hood. Morgan Le Fay has a cameo part, too, plus a lot of other well-known, and respected, Faery and Sidhe. Well, I believe, don't you? Clap your hands!

I know one of the legends Chris has incorporated in this series, that the Good Folk interfaced with humans in an attempt to keep the intruders out of England: Poul Anderson's *Midsummer's Tempest* being notable in employing it. But that only enriches the tapestry, as it were.

Mind you, Chris uses a lot of the not-nice eerie folk who were supposed to abound in those times — things that crawl out of graves and drag victims back into them, stuff of which nightmares are made — in some excellent and frightening panels by Bolton.

The hero of the tale, the eponymous Black Dragon who knoweth not his real nature, is James Dunreith, Duke of Ca'rynth. (I think I used that as a dragon's name once . . . anticipating?) He has returned to his native land upon the death of his liege-lord Henry, and is immediately embroiled in un-nicenesses of the "X-file" kind. (Well, we authors do get our material from a variety of sources, and if it works, why not?)

The lady fair, Ellianne de Valera, happens across our hero's path just after he has been reunited with his faithful henchman, Brian (Bri) Griffon, and that name is not without significance. He's also a very smart henchman and loyal follower and not without a few brains. I like that. The fair Ellianne just happens to be the daughter of James' best and closest friend whom he must now, on Eleanor's instructions, vet as to associations with black magicks.

Published first as a comics series in 1985, I'm delighted that *Black Dragon* is here in a more permanent form than the vulnerable paper books. Chris has arranged a complex plot with good dialogue as much in the period's speech as is easy to understand and Bolton with illustrations so remarkably photographic in their detail they only improve the sense of reality about the yarn.

Therefore, I can heartily commend you to read *The Black Dragon* and enjoy as I did.

Anne McCaffrey
Dragonhold-Underhill
Ireland

THE DAY HE HEARD OF HENRY'S DEATH, HE STARTED FOR HOME.
SO MUCH TIME HAD PASSED SINCE HIS EXILE BEGAN-- HE'D LOST TRACK OF THE YEARS-- HE THOUGHT IT WOULD BE SAFE.
HE WAS WRONG.
BOLTON ©

THEY'RE NOT GAINING-- BUT NEITHER AM I!
I'VE NO CHANCE OF LOSING THEM IN OPEN COUNTRY-- AND THERE ARE TOO MANY TO FIGHT--

-- BUT IF I CAN REACH THOSE TREES-- !

AIOWW!
NYAA

AAYHRRRRRRRRR
OU'RE DONE, ERETIC--
-- WITH NEITHER HORSE TO RIDE...
...NOR WEAPONS TO-- WHUNFLF!
I STILL POSSESS MY WITS, CHURL!

MORE THAN ENOUGH TO DEAL WITH THE LIKES OF YOU!

YARHAII!

OWH!

NOW, ENCHANTER, LET'S SEE YOU WORK YOUR EVIL--
-- WITH YOUR HEAD SEPARATED FROM YOUR NECK!!

HOLD, BERIC! YOU KNOW THE ORDERS.
PLAGUE TAKE 'EM! I'VE LOST TOO MANY GOOD COMRADES TODAY AT HIS HANDS! I SAY, HIS BLOOD FOR THEIRS!

AT THE PROPER PLACE, MY FRIEND, AND THE PROPER TIME.
SUPPOSE HE'S ALL THE STORIES SAY-- HAVE YOU CONSIDERED THAT?! THE PRIESTS KNOW THEIR BUSINESS, LEAVE HIM TO THEM.
BIND HIM TO A HORSE-- WE RIDE FOR WHITETHORNE ABBEY!

I AM NO THREAT TO YOU AND YOURS, PRIEST-- NEVER HAVE BEEN-- WHY COULDN'T YOU LEAVE WELL ENOUGH ALONE?
NO MAN-- NEITHER DUKE, A SUPPOSED PRINCE OF THE REALM, NOR EVEN A KING-- IS ABOVE THE LAW. HIS ROYAL MAJESTY *HENRY PLANTAGENET* BANISHED YOU ON PAIN OF DEATH. SINCE *RICHARD LION-HEART* HAS NOT PARDONED YOU, WE ARE MERELY PERFORMING OUR CIVIL DUTY AS LOYAL SUBJECTS.
THEN WHY AREN'T I IN THE TOWER, AWAITING THE *KING'S* PLEASURE?!
WE WOULD NOT PLACE ANY CHRISTIAN SOUL AT RISK, NECROMANCER, WHERE YOUR DEVIL'S ARTS MIGHT TEMPT IT FROM THE PATH OF RIGHTEOUSNESS.
MOST CONSIDERATE. TELL ME, HOW'D YOU KNOW WHERE I'D LAND? EVEN I WASN'T SURE TILL I CAME ASHORE.

THERE ARE THOSE AMONG OUR BRETHREN, GIFTED BY THE LORD, ABLE TO TRAVERSE THE SHADOW REALM. THEY DIVINED YOUR COMING.
THAT AMUSES YOU?

YOU DON'T PERCEIVE A SLIGHT IRONY, LORD ABBOTT, BETWEEN HOLY MOTHER CHURCH BURNING ME AT THE STAKE AS A SORCERER...
...AND USING A SORCERY OF ITS OWN TO HUNT ME DOWN?

OUR WORK IS BLESSED!
AND MINE ISN'T SORCERY!
FOOL! IT HAS NEVER BEEN THE WORK WE FEARED, BUT THE MAN HIMSELF! GREAT EVIL IS ABROAD ON THE LAND, JAMES DUNREITH, AND *YOU* ARE ITS CHAMPION --THE CATALYST THROUGH WHICH SATAN WILL ATTEMPT TO ACHIEVE DOMINION OVER THIS REALM!
THAT, WE WILL NEVER ALLOW! YOU WILL DIE AT DAWN. YOUR ASHES WILL BE PURIFIED AND SCATTERED THROUGHOUT THE LAND-- EVEN IN YOUR OWN DOMAIN--
--IT SHALL BE AS IF YOU HAD NEVER BEEN --*eh?!*
WHO'S THERE?!

BROTHER WILLIAM, IS THAT YOU-- ?!
THE MAN IS MAD!
AS MUCH AS I, FOR COMING HOME. I SHOULD HAVE STAYED AWAY, BUT I MISSED IT TOO MUCH -- THE PLACES, THE PEOPLE I LOVE -- WHAT'S THAT ?!
WELL --!
THEY DECIDED NOT TO WAIT TILL MORNING.
AT LEAST COLD STEEL'S A CLEANER, QUICKER END THAN THE FLAMES, I SUPPOSE I SHOULD BE GRATEFUL.
A PLAIN SURCOAT -- AM I NOT TO KNOW MY EXECUTIONER, SIR KNIGHT?
MUTE AS WELL.
AND IN A HURRY. I'LL NOT KEEP YOU THEN.
I HOPE YOUR BLADE'S KEEN -- I'VE NO HANKERING TO BE BUTCHERED.
THOSE BRAVE WORDS SHOULD DO MY LEGEND PROUD-- AFTER ALL, HOW ONE DIES SOMETIMES MATTERS AS MUCH AS THE DEATH ITSELF.
IN TRUTH, I'M A LITTLE AFRAID. I'VE SO OFTEN WONDERED ABOUT THIS FINAL MYSTERY. AT LAST, I'LL--
-- !?!

IS THIS SOME CRUEL JEST--?! AM I TO BURN?!!
ON YOUR FEET, DOG!
WHY?!
WALK OR DIE, THE CHOICE IS YOURS.
SINCE HIS INCARCERATION, HE'S HAD NEITHER FOOD NOR WATER...

...NOR HAVE HIS WOUNDS BEEN TENDED TO. HE'S BEEN CRUELLY TORTURED-- BY RIGHTS, HE SHOULDN'T EVEN BE ABLE TO STAND, MUCH LESS FOLLOW THE KNIGHT OUT HIS CELL DOOR.
BUT HE DOES.
THE MONKS-- THE MEN WHO CAPTURED ME-- ALL SLAIN!
WHO ARE YOU?! WHO SENT YOU?!!
HIS VOICE CRACKS AS HE SHRIEKS HIS QUESTIONS--
--HIS WEAKNESS SHAMING HIM--

-- BUT THE ONLY WORDS SPOKEN IN REPLY ARE...
MOUNT!
THEY'RE...TORCHING THE ABBEY--DESTROYING ALL EVIDENCE OF THEIR DEEDS.

WE'VE A LONG, HARD RIDE AHEAD, SORCERER.
IF YOU FALL, WE'LL LEAVE YOU WHERE YOU DROP.
NO DOUBT WITH A SPEAR THROUGH MY HEART...
...TO GUARANTEE MY SILENCE.

HO, THE KEEP! CALL THE PHYSICIAN TO THE YARD!
WE'VE A WOUNDED MAN HERE!!

I'LL CREDIT YOU FOR COURAGE, SCOT. I DIDN'T THINK YOU'D LAST.
TRUE PRAISE ...INDEED ...SIR KNIGHT.
...BUT THEN... ALWAYS WAS TOO STUBBORN... FOR... OWN GOOD...
HELP HIM DOWN, VILLEINS--AND GENTLY DOES IT! HE'S SORE HURT!

PUT HIM TO BED-- I'LL INFORM THE QUEEN.
A WASTE O' TIME AN' YEW ASK ME. THIS'UN WON'T LAST THE DAY.
CHRIST'S HOLY BONES, HE'S COLD AS ICE! AN' HE'S THE MAN WE'VE MOVED HEAVEN AN' EARTH T' SAVE-- HA!

THIS IS NOT REAL, IT CANNOT BE!
I SOAR -- TO THE ROOF OF CREATION AND BEYOND!
I KNOW I AM DYING -- ARE THESE THEN THE LAST MOMENTS OF MY LIFE, OR THE FIRST OF WHAT COMES AFTER? DO I APPROACH HEAVEN...
...OR HELL?
OR SOMETHING ELSE??? IN MY TRAVELS, I SAW MEN ABLE TO CAST OUT THEIR SOULS FROM THEIR BODIES -- THEY SPOKE OF REALMS BEYOND OUR OWN, MAGICKAL PLACES FILLED WITH STRANGE AND TERRIBLE CREATURES.
I TRIED TO FOLLOW, WITHOUT SUCCESS --
-- UNTIL TODAY.
UNLESS -- THIS IS A FEVER DREAM, A DESPERATE FANTASY CONJURED BY MY MIND TO EASE ITS PASSING.
HOW AM I TO KNOW, WHO IS THERE TO TELL ME?!
I FIND MYSELF DRAWN FROM LAND TO SEA, TOWARDS A VAST, MOUNTAINOUS ISLE.
I AM HARDLY THAT, O MAN.
A VOICE, NOT MY OWN -- BY ALL THAT'S HOLY!!
WHAT ARE YOU?!?

SALVATION.
DAMNATION.
THE CHOICE IS THINE.
I AM THAT WHICH THOU HAST E'ER KNOWN BUT NE'ER UNDERSTOOD, SENSED BUT NE'ER TOUCHED, SOUGHT BUT NE'ER FOUND. I AM THY SELF.
NO!
TRY AS THOU MIGHT, DO WHAT THOU WILT...
...I SHALL NOT BE DENIED.

NO!!
ITS BREATH-- FIRE-- I BURN!!!
YET... I LIVE!

HE SCREAMED, MASTER LABORDIER! I NEVER HEARD SUCH A CRY-- LOOK!
SANCTUS DEI-- C'EST IMPOSSIBLE! C'EST UN MIRACLE!!

HAVE YOU NO FAITH IN YOUR OWN ARTS, HEALER?
I... I...
HOLY MOTHER, PRESERVE US--
--HE IS A WIZARD!

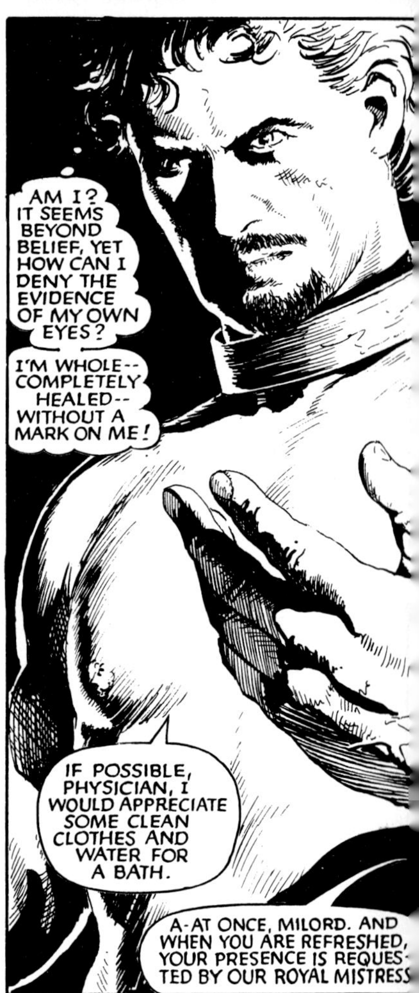
AM I? IT SEEMS BEYOND BELIEF, YET HOW CAN I DENY THE EVIDENCE OF MY OWN EYES?
I'M WHOLE-- COMPLETELY HEALED-- WITHOUT A MARK ON ME!
IF POSSIBLE, PHYSICIAN, I WOULD APPRECIATE SOME CLEAN CLOTHES AND WATER FOR A BATH.
A-AT ONCE, MILORD. AND WHEN YOU ARE REFRESHED, YOUR PRESENCE IS REQUESTED BY OUR ROYAL MISTRESS

HOW LIKE HER TO COUCH HER COMMAND AS THE MOST DECEPTIVELY COURTEOUS OF INVITATIONS. BUT MAKE NO MISTAKE, THAT WAS A COMMAND. REFUSAL IS NOT AN OPTION.
I'M HERE FOR A REASON. SHE WANTS SOMETHING -- BADLY, I'LL WAGER.
THIS WAY, MILORD. ALL IS PREPARED.
MOST GRACIOUS LADY-- JAMES LORD DUNREITH, DUKE OF CA'RYNTH.
WELCOME, JAMIE-- TO MY HEARTH AND TO MY LAND. YOU HAVE BEEN SORELY MISSED.
AND YOU, ELEANOR, ARE AS GRACIOUS AND BEAUTIFUL AS EVER.
THE ONE, PERHAPS, YOU SCOUNDREL. BUT I'VE LONG SINCE BECOME RESIGNED TO THE FADING OF THE OTHER.
THE YEARS, I SEE, HAVE BEEN FAR... KINDER TO YOU.
SIT, FILL YOUR BELLY! I'VE ALREADY DINED.
I WAS SORRY TO HEAR OF HENRY'S PASSING.
SAID LIKE A COURTIER. I'M NOT-- PRISON DOESN'T AGREE WITH ME.
ALTHOUGH RICHARD HELPED HIM ALONG, IT WAS HENRY'S TIME.
I THOUGHT THIS MORNING IT WAS MOST CERTAINLY YOURS. HOW KIND OF YOU TO PROVE ME WRONG.
OF COURSE, WHAT ELSE SHOULD ONE EXPECT FROM A WIZARD? THEN AGAIN, WHY WOULD SUCH A MAN ALLOW HIMSELF TO BE CAPTURED SO EASILY IN THE FIRST PLACE, AND TORTURED NEARLY UNTO DEATH?
OCCASIONALLY, MADAM, I SURPRISE EVEN MYSELF.
THE QUESTION IS, IN WHICH WAY?
IT WAS NO IDLE WHIM THAT SENT MY KNIGHTS TO SAVE YOU, DUNREITH. I REQUIRE YOUR SERVICES.
THERE IS REBELLION AFOOT IN THE WEST COUNTRY-- LED BY THE EARL OF GLENOWYN...
...EDMUND De VALERE!

I DON'T BELIEVE IT!
I KNOW EDMUND AS I DO MYSELF, I'LL STAKE MY LIFE ON HIS LOYALTY TO HENRY!

YOU'VE BEEN AWAY A LIFETIME, MY LORD, PEOPLE CHANGE. MORE-OVER, HENRY IS IN HIS GRAVE.
AND HIS HEIRS, BLESS THEIR CONNIVING, GREEDY HEARTS, CANNOT SEEM TO DECIDE ON THE PROPER SUCCESSION. RICHARD HOLDS THE CROWN, BUT JOHN WANTS IT, WHATEVER THE COST.
WITH THE LIONHEART IN ENGLAND, THERE WOULD BE NO PROBLEM.

BUT HE IS IN PALESTINE, HACKING HIS MERRY WAY THROUGH ANVILS TO IMPRESS THE INFIDELS.
SUCH INTERNECINE STRIFE BREEDS INSURREC-TION AS CORPSES DO PESTILENCE. EVERY BARON SEES THE POSSIBILITIES. ONLY DeVALERE IS ATTEMPTING TO SEIZE THEM, THOUGH HOW HE'D HOLD THE THRONE, ASSUMING HE WON IT, IS BEYOND ME. THE NOBILITY WOULD NO MORE READILY ACCEPT HIM AS KING THAN THEY DID AS FELLOW PEER.

WERE THESE ORDINARY RUMORS, JAMES, I'D DEAL WITH HIM MYSELF. I'VE LED AND CRUSHED MORE THAN MY SHARE OF SUCH ADVENTURES.
HOWEVER-- THERE ARE INDICATIONS EDMOND IS TRAFFICKING IN THE *ANCIENT ARTS*.

YOU WERE THE BEST OF FRIENDS, HE WILL ACCEPT YOU INTO HIS CAMP WITHOUT QUESTION. IF THE MAN IS INNOCENT, OR ALL HE PLANS IS SIMPLE TREASON, LEAVE HIM TO ME-- YOU NEED NOT REPORT BACK OR TAKE ANY ACTION.

BUT IF BANEFUL MAGICKS *ARE* INVOLVED, I WANT IT *STOPPED*.
NOW AND FOREVER.

NOT MERELY JUDAS, THEN, BUT CAIN.
YOU'RE VERY SURE OF ME, ELEANOR-- SUPPOSE I JOIN HIM?
LIKE EDMUND, I SWORE MY OATH TO HENRY-- I'VE NO GREAT LOVE FOR HIS SONS. NORMAN BARONS AND NORMAN CLERGY-- NORMAN *HATE*-- STRIPPED ME OF LANDS AND TITLES, BRANDED ME OUTLAW AND DROVE ME INTO EXILE!
WHY SHOULD I CARE WHAT HAPPENS TO THEM, MUCH LESS LIFT EVEN A FINGER ON THEIR BEHALF?

DAMN YOU!
IF THE PLANTAGENET DYNASTY WERE THE ONLY THING AT RISK, I'D'VE LET YOU ROT! I FEAR FOR THE *REALM*, DUNREITH--
--FOR ALL **BRITAIN!!**

I TURN TO YOU BECAUSE I'VE NO ALTERNATIVE-- PRAYING THAT THE YEARS HAVE NOT TAINTED THE SENSE OF HONOR I REMEMBER SO WELL, NOR YOUR LOVE FOR THIS LAND.
IN RETURN, I OFFER CA'RYNTH.

MY DOMAIN, LADY, IS NO MORE YOURS TO *GIVE* THAN YOUR HUSBAND'S TO TAKE.

IT IS PART OF THIS ISLAND, AS ARE *YOU!*
A HUNDRED YEARS HAVE PASSED SINCE THE CONQUEST, AND NORMAN AND SAXON ARE STILL AT EACH OTHER'S THROATS. BUT WE ARE HERE TO STAY, MY LORD DUKE-- WE HAVE PUT OUR ROOTS DEEP INTO THIS ISLE-- EACH SUCCEEDING GENERATION BINDS OUR PEOPLES CLOSER TOGETHER. EVENTUALLY, WE WILL BE *ONE!*
TO CAST US OUT WILL OPEN WOUNDS IN THE BODY POLITIC NOTHING WILL HEAL!

ENGLAND WILL NO LONGER BE A NATION, BUT A *SPLINTERED* COLLECTION OF WARRING TRIBES, FIT ONLY FOR PLUNDER. UNTIL ANOTHER CONQUEROR MAKES HIS ENTRANCE-- IS THAT WHAT YOU WANT?!
NO.
I STILL BELIEVE YOU'RE WRONG ABOUT EDMOND. BUT I OWE IT TO HIM AND YOU-- AND HENRY-- TO PROVE IT.

AND SO, THE FOLLOWING MORNING...
GODSPEED AND GOOD FORTUNE, MY LORD OF CA'RYNTH.
MAY YOU FIND THE DESTINY YOU DESERVE.

THE ROAD FORKS-- SOONER THAN I EXPECTED-- I CAN TURN WEST TOWARDS EDMUND...
...OR NORTH FOR HOME.
AND WHO'S TO STOP ME IF I DO?

I'M ALONE, RIDING A SOUND HORSE, WITH A STURDY BLADE AND A HUNDRED GOLD CROWNS TO GET ME OUT OF TROUBLE.
ELEANOR PROMISED ME THE REVOCATION OF MY BANISHMENT, RESTORATION OF ALL TITLES, LANDS, POSSESSIONS, PARDON FOR ANY "CRIMES." THE PLEDGE WAS MADE IN GOOD FAITH, BUT NOWHERE IS IT BINDING ON HER SONS--OR THEIRS.

WHO AM I FOOLING? ELEANOR KNOWS ME TOO WELL.
I GAVE MY WORD.

"I KNOW EDMUND AS I DO MYSELF." THAT MEANT SOMETHING YESTERDAY.
THE DUNREITH COAT OF ARMS IS AN EBONY DRAGON RAMPANT ON A SILVER FIELD. I ALWAYS ASSUMED THAT WAS SYMBOLIC-- DOLT!
LISTEN TO YOURSELF-- YOU'LL BE SEEING ELVES AND FAIRIES NEXT AND CHASING UNICORNS. AND YOU CALL YOURSELF AN EDUCATED MAN!
IF YOU'VE LEARNED ANYTHING IN YOUR TRAVELS, IT'S THAT WHAT HAPPENS IN THE MIND IS A PRODUCT OF THE MIND, NOTHING MORE! EVERY STORY I HEARD ALONG THE SILK ROAD--FROM DAMASCUS TO CATHAY-- EVERY WONDER I BEHELD, HAD A RATIONAL EXPLANATION. SO DOES THIS.
IS MY HEALING FORCE-- FANTASTIC AS IT SEEMS-- ANY LESS NATURAL THAN THE ABILITY OF INDIAN FAKIRS TO SLEEP ON BEDS OF NAILS?
BUT WHAT MADE IT HAPPEN NOW?! I'VE BEEN WOUNDED BEFORE-- TOO OFTEN TO COUNT-- WHERE WAS THE BLOODY MAGIC THEN?!!
PROBABLY HERE, WAITING FOR ME TO COME HOME.
SO MANY YEARS I'VE BEEN GONE-- A LIFETIME, AS ELEANOR SAID-- I'D FORGOTTEN HOW SWEET THE AIR IS IN SPRING. THERE'S NOWHERE ON EARTH QUITE THE SAME.
WHAT'S THAT, WOOD-SMOKE--?! IT'S A COOK-FIRE-- SOME-ONE'S UP AHEAD!

BRI?!? BRIAN GRIFFON, IS THAT YOU?!!
AN' WHO ELSE?
G'D MORROW T' YOU, M'LORD.
SAINTS BE PRAISED, YOU LOOK THE SAME AS EVER.
AS ETERNAL AS A ROCK, THA'S ME.

WHAT BRINGS YOU SO FAR FROM THE HIGHLANDS?!
I HAD A DREAM. AND WHEN THE DRAGON CALLS, THE GRIFFON EVER ANSWERS.

YOUR DREAM TOLD YOU I WAS COMING, AND BY WHICH ROAD?
AYE.
AND HOW HAS THE GRIFFON FARED? IS ALL WELL,
NO COMPLAINTS, SAVE THAT HE'S BEEN TOO LONG FROM THE DRAGON'S SIDE. YOU SHOULD NA' HA' LEFT ME, JAMIE.
YOU HAD FAMILY, BRI, MY EXILE WAS FOR LIFE.

LATER...
...THAT'S ALL THE QUEEN TOLD ME.
YOU'LL FORGIVE ME, JAMIE-- I KNOW YOU TWO WERE UNCOMMON CLOSE-- BUT THE LORD EDMUND EVER HAD A DANGEROUS WILD STREAK IN HIM.
IS THERE ANY WONDER?

HE'S THE BASTARD SON OF A NORMAN LORD AND HIS WELSH MISTRESS. THE ONLY REASON HE HOLDS THE TITLE IS BECAUSE NO LEGITIMATE HEIRS SURVIVED TO CLAIM IT.
HE WAS OSTRACISED AT COURT-- I WAS THE FIRST TO SPEAK TO HIM AND HIS ONLY FRIEND. EVEN WHEN HE'D WON A PLACE OF HONOR AT HENRY'S SIDE, HE WAS NO MORE THAN TOLERATED.
YOU WERE A BETTER-- TRUER-- FRIEND THAN HE DESERVED.

WHAT HARM DID HE EVER DO YOU, BRI, THAT YOU SHOULD SPEAK SO?
OR IS IT YOUR DREAMS THAT CONDEMN HIM?!
DO NOT SCOFF, MY LORD, ABOUT THINGS YOU DO NOT KNOW --D'YOU HEAR, JAMIE?!!

"THE SOUNDS OF BATTLE!"

THERE ARE TOO MANY BRIGANDS-- THE ESCORT'S BEING SLAUGHTERED!
WE'LL HAVE TO MAKE A RUN FOR IT! IF WE CAN REACH SOME HORSES--!
YRRAAA!!

THEY'LL KILL US!
PERHAPS-- BUT IF WE STAY, AND LET THEM TAKE US, THEY'RE SURE TO DO FAR WORSE.
ELLI, BEHIND YOU!

YER A FAIR YOUNG RUFFIAN WI' THAT BLADE, SQUIRE!
CUT MY TOBY'S EYE Y'DID, AN' SCARRED HIM F'R LIFE. WERE A PRETTY BOY, TOO, PROUD OF HIS LOOKS.
IF YOU WISH, DOG, I'LL DO THE SAME FOR YOU!

G-OUGHH*

RIDERS!
SCATTER THEM, BRI--DO AS MUCH DAMAGE AS YOU CAN--DON'T GIVE THEM A CHANCE TO THINK!

A LARGE BAND--SURPRISINGLY WELL-ARMED FOR ORDINARY BRIGANDS AND DESPERATE, TOO, IF THEY'RE WILLING TO TAKE ON A NOBLE'S CARAVAN.
I'M COUNTING ON SPEED AND SURPRISE TO DECEIVE THEM INTO BELIEVING THERE ARE MORE OF US. IF THEY REALIZE WE'RE BUT TWO, THINGS COULD GET VERY NASTY INDEED.

AWAY FROM YON WAGON, Y' POXY GIT!
YOWH!
MERCY, I BEG YOU!

YOU'LL GET WHAT Y'GAVE, LADDIE-BUCK!
AYE, RUN F'R THE WOODS, THOSE O' YOU STILL ABLE!
IF YOU'VE HALF A BRAIN B'TWEEN THE LOT O' YOU, YOU'LL NO' COME BACK!

WATCH THE TREE-LINE, BRI, WHILE I SEE TO ANY SURVIVORS.
I DOUBT WE'LL BE SO LUCKY.

ISABEL, WE'RE--!?!
Oh...
...YOU POOR DEAR--FORGIVE ME, BELOVED FRIEND, I PLEDGED MY LIFE IN YOUR DEFENSE.

MAY THE LORD WELCOME YOU TO HIS GRAVE WITH FLIGHTS OF ANGELS, YOU WHO THOUGHT AND DID NONE HARM.
YOU CAME TOO LATE, SIR KNIGHT.
THE LADY ISABEL de LACEY IS DEAD.

BLOODY HELL -- I THOUGHT THE ROADS WERE SAFER'N THIS, SAVE IN SHERWOOD, UP NOTTINGHAM WAY.
YON SQUIRE'S IT. I'VE GOT HIM A HORSE.
ANY SURVIVORS?

GOOD MAN. GATHER WHAT WEAPONS YOU NEED, LAD, AND WE'LL BE ON OUR WAY.
YOU CAN'T LEAVE, NOT YET!
THOSE BRIGANDS WON'T STAY CHASED AWAY FOR LONG.

SHE WAS MY FRIEND.
I SHAN'T LEAVE HER...
...UNTIL SHE'S HAD A PROPER CHRISTIAN BURIAL.

THAT'S AN INDULGENCE WE CAN ILL AFFORD, BOY!
NOW CLIMB ON THAT HORSE AND RIDE!
LET ME GO!

BY THE SACRED STONES!
LAY HAND ON ME ONCE MORE WITHOUT MY LEAVE, SIRRAH--
--AND BE PREPARED TO LOSE IT!

YOU'RE IN TOO MUCH OF A HURRY-- OR YOU'RE TOO AFRAID-- THEN LEAVE! RUN AWAY!
I'LL TAKE MY CHANCES BY MYSELF!
IF YOU STAY, SILLY GIRL, YOU'LL HAVE NO CHANCE! DEATH IS THE BEST YOU CAN HOPE FOR-- ESPECIALLY IF THEY DISCOVER YOU'RE A WOMAN!
ARGKH-- I'M IN NO MOOD FOR A DEBATE--
--BRIAN, HER KNIFE!
TOSS IT HERE, JAMIE, I'LL KEEP IT SAFE!
NN--OH!
BEHAVE YOUR-SELF NOW, LASS!
NO, PLEASE! DO NOT DO THIS! ISABEL!
ISABEL!
SHE'S BEYOND HEARING. BEYOND PAIN. SHE'S FOUND HER ETERNAL PEACE-- OUR INTENT IS TO ENSURE NEITHER YOU NOR WE JOIN HER.
BRIAN, I DON'T WANT TO SPEND TONIGHT IN THE OPEN.
I KNOW OF AN INN ABOUT TWO HOURS FARTHER ON, JAMIE-- HOW'S THAT?!
M'LORD KNOWS HIS BUSINESS, LASS-- BEST TRUST HIM. Y'WON'T BE SORRY.

AND SO, AFTER A HARD RIDE...
TAVERN
I TELL YOU, THE ARROGANCE OF THESE SAXON PEASANTS IS BEYOND BELIEF.
THAT'S TRUTH! POACHING'S BAD ENOUGH, BUT TO TAKE THE KING'S DEER!
SO WHAT THEN, BURGO?!
CLOT! WE SPARED BARON RICHARD THE BOTHER OF HOLDING A TRIAL.
STRUNG THE BUGGER UP!
Y' SHOULD EAT, LASS. Y' NEED T' KEEP UP YUIR STRENGTH.
I'M NOT HUNGRY, THANK YOU, MASTER GRIFFON.
SUIT YOURSELF.

ISABEL WAS A GOOD SOUL-- GENTLE AND KIND-- SHE DESERVED BETTER.
FROM LIFE, AND DEATH!
MOST DO.
YOUR WORDS, SIRRAH, ARE AS CRUEL AS YOUR DEEDS.

REALLY? THE ONLY DEED I RECALL OF LATE IS SAVING YOU! EVIDENTLY, THAT WAS A MISTAKE-- WE SHOULD HAVE LEFT YOU AND CARRIED OFF YOUR LADY'S CORPSE.
HAVE YOU NO FEELINGS...

..NOT EVEN THE SMALLEST SHRED OF COMMON DECENCY? BAD ENOUGH THAT CHILD WAS SENT TO OUR MAKER UNSHRIVEN, CARRYING THE FULL BURDEN OF HER SINS!
SO WONDERFUL A CHILD HAS SINS ?
JAMIE, FORBEAR--!
LASS, HARD AS IT IS TO ACCEPT, WE'D ONLY'VE SACRIFICED OURSELVES F'R NAUGHT. WHATEVER WE DID, THE BRIGANDS WOULD'VE DUG UP HER BODY, T' STRIP IT O' GOWN AN' JEWELS.
THEY'VE NO RESPECT F'R THE LIVING, LESS F'R THE DEAD.

NO!
OH, MY GOD --MY GOD!

I'M SORRY. I NEVER MEANT TO HURT YOU, PLEASE BELIEVE THAT.
IN MY TRAVELS, I'VE SEEN TOO MUCH OF THE WORST HUMANITY HAS TO OFFER. SOME OF IT, I FEAR, HAS RUBBED OFF ON ME.
BUT BRIAN IS RIGHT.

I WISH WE COULD HAVE SAVED YOUR FRIEND AS WELL. BUT SHE WAS BEYOND HARM; MY-- OUR-- RESPONSIBILITY WAS TO THE LIVING.
IT'S NO CRIME, LASS, THAT YOU SURVIVED AND SHE DID NOT.
BUT IT FEELS SO.
I KNOW.
AS A KNIGHT, I SUPPOSE YOU DO.

I THOUGHT... I WAS BRAVER-- AND... STRONGER --THAN THIS.
YOU FOUGHT AS WELL AS ANY SOLDIER, YOU'VE NOTHING TO BE ASHAMED OF.
NOT SO. YOU SAVED MY LIFE, AND I HAVEN'T EVEN HAD THE GRACE...
...TO THANK YOU.

I HAVEN'T EVEN TOLD YOU MY NAME.
I AM *ELLIANNE De VALERE.* MY FATHER IS...
... THE EARL OF GLENOWYN.
YOU KNOW HIM?
WE'RE... OLD FRIENDS--

--THOUGH IT'S BEEN A WHILE SINCE WE LAST SAW EACH OTHER.
INDEED, IT WAS BEFORE YOU WERE BORN.
I BEG YOUR PARDON!?!
WHOOOPS?!?

OH, HOW CLUMSY OF ME *hic* DIDN'T SEE YOU, DIDN'T MEAN TO, SO *DREADFULLY* SORRY!
Pig.
NO HARM DONE, SIR KNIGHT, NO OFFENSE TAKEN.

WELLWELLWELLWELLWELL, WHAT *HAVE* WE HERE?! A MOST SWEET AND COMELY YOUNG *hic* THING, I DO DECLARE!
YOU'VE WON MY HEART, WENCH-- FAVOR ME WITH A SMILE, A KISS...
... A TUMBLE, HEY?!
WHAT HO, *MES BRAVES?!* HOW UTTERLY *CHARMING*--

-- I'VE DRAWN FIRE TO HER CHEEKS!
A TRIFLE INAPPROPRIATE-- SUCH MODEST BEHAVIOR--
--FOR ONE SO *gighicgle* *IMMODESTLY* DRESSED, BUT LET IT PASS.
YOUNG MAN, YOU'RE DISTURBING THE YOUNG LADY. AND ME.
PLEASE GO.

AM I DISTURBING YOU, MY DARLING? HOW CAN THAT BE, WHEN ANY FOOL CAN SEE YOUR LIPS YEARN FOR MI
IIEIEEE!
WATCH YUIR STEP, SIR-- 'PEARS T' ME THE DRINK'S GONE T' YUIR HEAD.
WHAT THERE IS OF IT.
SIR JAMES, I WANT NO TROUBLE--!
NOR DO I.
HE TRIPPED ME!
BY CHRIST, I'LL HAVE THE VILLEIN'S HEART FOR HIS EFFRONTERY!
AND YOURS AS WELL, WHORESON, IF YOU SEEK TO DEFEND HIM!

SHEATHE YOUR BLADE, SIR KNIGHT.
IN YOUR POXY GUT!
MAKE NO RASH PROMISES, LAD-- OR THREATS.

THIS LADY IS IN MY CHARGE, AND UNDER MY PROTECTION.
DO NOT FORCE ME TO CROSS SWORDS WITH YOU...

...OR ONE OF US WILL SURELY DIE.

MY SQUIRE IS INDEED A CLUMSY, ILL-MANNERED, DULL-WITTED LOUT, HARDLY WORTH YOUR TROUBLE. LEAVE HIS CHASTISEMENT TO ME.
CHOP 'IM, BURGO!
FIGHT! FIGHT! FIGHT!
ARROGANT SCOTS SWINE, TEACH 'EM A LESSON!

THERE'S NO NEED FOR VIOLENCE.
WE ARE ALL BELTED KNIGHTS, SWORN TO THE SERVICE OF GOD AND OUR KING-- IN THAT, WE ARE BROTHERS.
IT WOULD BE A SHAME TO SPOIL SO FAIR AN EVENING-- AND THE GOOD FELLOWSHIP ENJOYED BY YOU AND YOUR COMPANIONS-- WITH BLOOD.
WELL... I S'POSE... I, er...

BY WAY OF BALANCING THE SCALES, PLEASE ALLOW ME TO PAY FOR YOUR MEAL.
YESSS...
...YES!
KIND OF YOU, SIR, VERY GENEROUS --MUCH APPRECIATED!

YOU LETTING HIM OFF, BURGO, JUST LIKE THAT?!
HE'S AN OLD MAN, STEPHEN, LEAVE HIM BE!
WHAT ABOUT THE GIRL?! I'M IN THE MOOD FOR FUN!

SEEK IT ELSEWHERE.

THE HELL WITH IT, STEPHEN-- THERE'S PLENTY MORE LIKE HER, AND WILLING, TO BOOT!
WATCH YOUR STEP, THOUGH, SIRRAH! I KNOW YOUR FACE, I'VE MARKED IT WELL! CROSS MY ROAD AGAIN...
... AN' I'LL NOT BE SO FORGIVING!

I'LL REMEMBER.
THANK'EE, SIR, THANK'EE KINDLY! I WERE SURE MY PLACE'D BE WRECKED!
THEY BE FAIR GENTLEMEN, MOST O' THE TIME, BUT THEY GOT TOO MUCH DRINK IN 'EM, MADE 'EM A WEE BIT UGLY.
I NOTICED.
MIGHT I INQUIRE, SIR, 'BOUT YOUR PLANS...?

YOU NEED NOT WORRY, LANDLORD, WE'LL BE GONE COME SUNRISE. YOUR PATRONS WILL HAVE TO FIND OTHERS FOR THEIR SPORT.
AN' THEY WILL, HAVE NO DOUBT O' THAT, SIR, MORE'S THE PITY.
THIS SHOULD COVER OUR MEALS AND A NIGHT'S LODGING.
MOST GENEROUS, SIR! I'LL HAVE THE BEST IN THE HOUSE PREPARED STRAIGHTAWAY!

I WAS CERTAIN THERE'D BE BLOOD-SHED.
NO, THEY WEREN'T REALLY IN THE MOOD-- JUST BOYS, BORED, LOOKING FOR FUN.
IF I'D BEEN ALONE...
BUT YOU WEREN'T. ELLIANNE, WE'RE BOUND GLENOWYN WAY. IF YOU'LL HAVE US, WE'LL BE HAPPY TO ACT AS YOUR ESCORT.
I'D LIKE THAT, SIR JAMES, VERY MUCH.

LATER...
TWENTY-FIVE YEARS AND SO LITTLE HAS CHANGED. ELEANOR WAS RIGHT, THE OLD HATREDS STILL RUN DEEP. HOW HARD IT MUST HAVE BEEN FOR EDMUND...
...DENIED BY WELSH AND NORMAN BOTH.
AM I MAD TO OFFER MY FRIEND-SHIP TO HIS DAUGHTER? SHE COULD BE INVOLVED. ON THE OTHER HAND, WHAT BETTER WAY TO GET CLOSE TO EDMUND?

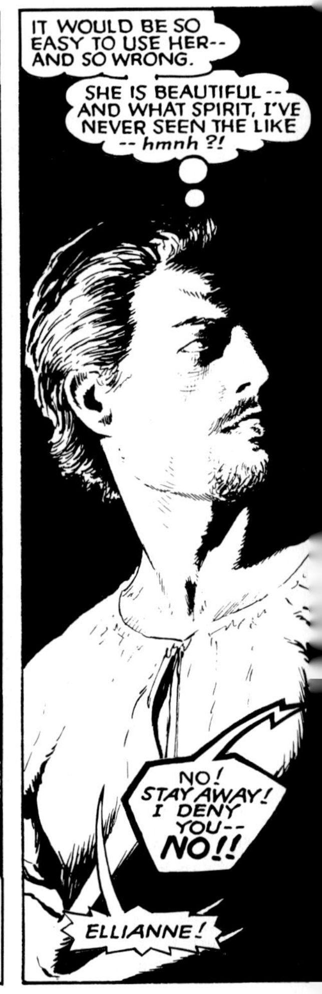
IT WOULD BE SO EASY TO USE HER-- AND SO WRONG.
SHE IS BEAUTIFUL-- AND WHAT SPIRIT, I'VE NEVER SEEN THE LIKE -- *hmnh* ?!
NO! STAY AWAY! I DENY YOU-- **NO!!**
ELLIANNE!

IF THOSE KNIGHTS--?!
ELLIANNE-- WHAT IS IT, WHAT'S WRONG?!!

DEMONS!

HORRIBLE-- AWFUL-- *THINGS,* CROWDING ALL ABOUT ME...
...CLAIMING ME FOR THEIR *VERY OWN!*
ELLIANNE--?!!
SIR JAMES-- *THANK HEAVEN!* I THOUGHT-- I... I FEARED--!
ARE YOU ALL RIGHT?! WHAT POSSESSED YOU, CHILD, A NIGHT-MARE?!

I WAS ASLEEP. IT MUST HAVE BEEN.
BUT EVERYTHING SEEMED SO... REAL!
THE LAND WAS DRENCHED IN BLOOD, THICK WITH ROTTING CORPSES.
I... BATHED IN IT.

THE BASILISK COULD NOT HAVE BEEN MORE FEARSOME, NOR MORE CRUEL. I... TORE THE HEARTS FROM LIVING BEASTS AND FEASTED 'TIL MY GUTS ACHED WITH FULLNESS.
I WAS THE CAUSE OF THIS CARNAGE. I *REVELLED* IN IT.

GOD FORGIVE ME...
... I HUNGERED FOR MORE.
LOOK AROUND--THE WORLD IS AS SAFE AND SANE AS EVER...
CAN THE SAME BE SAID FOR *ME?!*
YOU *DREAMED,* THAT IS ALL. IT HAS NO POWER TO DO YOU HARM, UN-LESS YOU LET IT.
EASY FOR YOU TO SAY.
SHALL I STAY WITH YOU, THEN...
...IN CASE DREAMS--OR DEMONS--RETURN

PRAY SO-- AWWWN
--WITH ALL MY HEART.
EXCEPT... I DREAMED OF ISABEL'S MURDER...
...AND THAT CAME TRUE.

THE DAYS AND LEAGUES THAT FOLLOW PASS UNEVENTFULLY. ELLI'S SLEEP IS NO LONGER TROUBLED; INDEED, SHE FINDS SMILES-- EVEN LAUGHTER-- SPRINGING MORE AND MORE READILY TO HER LIPS.
WE'RE RIDING AN OLD ROMAN ROAD, MILADY.
YOU CAN STILL SEE SIGNS OF IT, AFTER NEAR A THOUSAND YEARS.

THA' OLD BASTARD FULVIUS MARCUS, HE BUILDS THINGS TO LAST!
MASTER GRIFFON, YOU SPEAK AS THOUGH YOU AND HE WERE...
...FRIENDS.

WHAT AN ODD MAN.
NO MORESO THAN I.
I THINK OF HIM AS AN OAK; SOLID, STRONG, ETERNALLY UNCHANGING-- THE SAME AS FAR BACK AS I CAN REMEMBER-- AND FOREVER BY MY SIDE...
...'TIL I MET YOUR FATHER
I'M AS TERRIFIED OF THAT REUNION AS I AM EAGER FOR IT.
I WAS LITTLE MORE THAN A BABE WHEN I WAS FOSTERED TO QUEEN ELEANOR'S HOUSEHOLD--MY MOTHER BLESS HER SOUL, DIED IN CHILDBIRTH-

-- I HAVEN'T SEEN LORD EDMUND IN AGES. SUPPOSE I PROVE A DISAPPOINTMENT TO HIM?
THERE ISN'T A MAN ALIVE WHO CAN GAZE ON YOU, MILADY, AND NOT BE SMITTEN.
INCLUDING YOU, SIR KNIGHT?

Ah, DUNREITH, ART DAFT?!
YOU BOTH THINK THIS NO MORE'N AN INNOCENT FLIRTATION, BUT IT'S LONG PAST THA', I FEAR. I'TRUTH, SHE IS AN ENTRANCING GIRL AND IF E'ER TWO SOULS SEEMED MADE FOR EACH OTHER...
BUT YOU'RE ON THE QUEEN'S BUSINESS, MY NOBLE LORD. THE LASS MAY WELL BE PART OF HER FATHER'S TREASON
AN' THAT BE SO SHE MUST SHARE HIS FATE.

WHO AUGHT YOU TO RIDE-- 'VE RARELY SEEN MEN HANDLE A HORSE, OR BLADE, SO WELL?
THE QUEEN.
OF COURSE, I SHOULD HAVE KNOWN.
I CAN READ AND WRITE, AND SPEAK LATIN AND FRENCH. I KNOW HISTORY AND MATHEMATICS, A SMATTERING OF SCIENCES. I CAN EVEN COOK.
THANKS TO HER MAJESTY, I AM POSSESSED OF A SCORE OF TALENTS THAT-- EXCEPTING PERHAPS THE LAST--

-- I SHALL NEVER AGAIN USE.
FOR WHAT NEED HAS A DUTIFUL WIFE FOR LETTERS, OR ANY SUCH LEARNING? ELEANOR MAY LIVE AMONG THE STARS-- AND I, LUCKY ENOUGH TO FLY BESIDE HER FOR A TIME-- BUT I MUST NOW RETURN TO EARTH.
BLEAK THOUGHTS.
BLEAK PROSPECTS. I AM OF AGE-- MOST OF MY FEW FRIENDS ARE ALREADY BETROTHED OR WED--

WHY ELSE UMMON ME OME SO UDDENLY AVE FOR A ARRIAGE?
ONLY THE MOST AMBITIOUS OF MEN WOULD SEEK MY HAND, AND THEN ONLY TO LAY CLAIM TO MY FATHER'S RANK AND DOMAIN. SUCH A HUSBAND WILL NOT LOVE ME NOR, I THINK, WOULD I WISH TO CARE FOR HIM.
YOU COULD BE WRONG.

JAMIE-- TO ME!

IT IS HE!

THE YOUNG PRINCE HATH RETURNED, AS PROPHECY AND SIGNS FORETOLD--
--GODDESS HA' MERCY ON US ALL...
...AND ON THE LAND!
GASP!?!
THE ABBEY OF THE BLESSED VIRGIN!
YOU KNOW THIS PLACE?!
KING HENRY IMPRISONED ELEANOR NOT FAR FROM HERE, BEFORE SENDING HER TO SALISBURY TOWER. THIS WAS WHERE I WENT TO SCHOOL.
A LEAGUE BEYOND THESE WOODS LIES THE RIVER THAT MARKS THE EASTERN BOUNDRY OF GLENOWYN, MY FATHER'S DOMAIN.

WHO COULD HAVE DONE SUCH A THING-- THIS PLACE HELD NO RICHES, SAVE IN BOOKS AND KNOWLEDGE.
BRIAN, SEARCH THE RUINS AS BEST YOU CAN, I'LL KEEP WATCH. BE QUICK, MY FRIEND, THIS WAS RECENTLY DONE. THOSE RESPONSIBLE MAY STILL BE ABOUT.
AYE-- THOUGH I DOUBT WE'LL FIND ANYTHING WORTH THE EFFORT. THE SWINE DID A THOROUGH JOB.
I PRAY THE REVEREND SISTERS ESCAPED.
NO BODIES, NO BLOOD-- MOST LIKELY THEY DID, UNLESS THE RAIDERS CARRIED THEM OFF.
THE ABBEY WAS TAKEN WI'OUT MUCH OF A FIGHT. TRACKS INDICATE A FAIR-SIZED BAND O' RAIDERS --TOO MANY, I'M THINKIN', FOR OUTLAWS. THERE'S NA' BEEN MARAUDIN' LIKE THIS ACROSS THE LAND SINCE BEFORE THE CONQUEST.
STRIPPED BARE, JAMIE --THEY EVEN STOLE THE CHAPEL CRUCIFIX.
A SCREAM-- THE SISTERS, D'YOU HEAR?!!
THEY'RE CLOSE BY, IN AGONY! THEY'RE BEING TORTURED!
ELLIANNE-- STOP!
YOU LITTLE FOOL-- COME BACK!
YOU CAN'T HELP THEM, YOU'LL ONLY GET YOURSELF KILLED!

ELLIANNE-- !?!
HERE, SIR JAMES-- LISTEN TO THEIR CRIES, THEY TEAR AT MY VERY SOUL! THEY'RE *HERE!*

THE CIRCLE IS EMPTY, LASS, THE HILL-TOP AS DESERTED AS THE ABBEY.
HOW CAN THAT BE?! THE VOICES-- ?!!
WHAT VOICES?! THERE'S NO WIND, NO BIRDSONG, NOT EVEN THE BUZZ OF INSECTS-- THE SILENCE IS NEAR ABSOLUTE.
OH--
--JAMIE--
--LOOK!

BROTHER PAUL -- THE NUN'S CONFESSOR -- HE G-G-GAVE ME MY FIRST COMMUNION.
Oh, GOD -- OH, GOD -- HE WAS THE KINDEST OF MEN, HOW COULD YOU PERMIT SUCH A THING?!!
A QUESTION I TOO OFTEN ASK MYSELF.
AND EACH TIME, MY FAITH FADES A LITTLE MORE.
'TIL
ODAY,
T LONG
LAST,
NONE
EEMS
LEFT.
THE GOOD FRIAR'S DEAD -- THERE'S NO ONE ELSE HERE WITH US -- YET THE CRIES ARE LOUDER THAN EVER!
THEY COME FROM WITHIN THIS CIRCLE.
I CAN'T HEAR THEM.
I'M NOT LYING -- NOR AM I MAD!
I DIDN'T SAY YOU WERE!
ONE WAY OR THE OTHER, THE ANSWERS LIE WITHIN.
THIS, TOO, IS HOLY GROUND, CONSECRATED TO THE OLD RELIGION -- BY THE LOOKS OF IT, AS ANCIENT AS STONEHENGE -- THAT'S WHY THE ABBEY WAS BUILT AT THE FOOT OF ITS HILL, YOUR REVEREND SISTERS HOPED THOSE WHO FOLLOWED THE OLD WAYS AND WORSHIPPED HERE WOULD, IN TIME, TURN TO THE NEW FAITH, CHRIST.
DO YOU FOLLOW THOSE PAGAN WAYS, SIR KNIGHT?
I FOLLOW NOTHING.
STAY BACK, WELL OUTSIDE THE SARCEN STONES -- YOU, TOO, BRIAN. WHATEVER HAPPENS TO ME, YOU AT LEAST SHOULD BE SPARED.

THERE'S A PATTERN TO THIS I'VE SEEN BEFORE.
WHAT DO YOU MEAN?! SIR JAMES, CAN WE NOT CUT DOWN THE FRIAR--?!
IN A MOMENT, WHEN WE'RE CERTAIN IT'S SAFE.
HOLD HER, BRI! KEEP HER BY YOU!

PATCHES OF DISCOLORED EARTH BENEATH EACH CARDINAL STONE. AS FRESHLY DUG...
...AS THE ABBEY WAS FRESHLY BURNED.
DAMN!
ELLIANNE, HOW MANY NUNS RESIDED AT BLESSED MARY'S?

WHEN LAST I VISITED, THERE WERE TWELVE, INCLUDING THE LADY ABBESS--WHY?!
BEST LOOK AWAY, GIRL, THIS BE NOT FOR DECENT EYES.
I WILL NOT, NOR WILL I LEAVE! TELL ME, JAMES--WHAT HAVE YOU FOUND?

TWELVE STONES, TWELVE SISTERS.
NO!

PROBABLY BURIED ALIVE.
AN ACT OF SUPREMELY CALCULATED CRUELTY-- I CAN GUESS AS TO THE PURPOSE...
NO!
MERCIFUL CHRIST--
--JAMIE, BEHIND YOU!

WHA--?!?
IMPOSSIBLE!?!

THIS CAN'T BE HAPPENING!

I'M BEING PULLED INTO SOLID GROUND!
BUT WHAT POWER-- WHAT BEINGS--?!

GOD--

--MY GOD!?!

CAN'T BREATHE--!
CAN HARDLY MOVE!
THE GHOULS--LIKE QUICK-SILVER--CLAWS TEARING IRON MAIL AS EASILY AS FLESH!
I'M DONE --ALL MY KNOWLEDGE, MY EXPERIENCE-- USELESS AGAINST SUCH CREATURES!
NOT SO.
MADNESS!
OH YE OF LITTLE FAITH--!
HAST FORGOT ME ALREADY, YOUNGLING?

THE SIZE OF THE THING-- IT'S FAR LARGER THAN WHEN WE MET BEFORE!
WHERE AM I?! WHAT ARE YOU?!!
DOST FEAR ME, MAN-CHILD?
AYE.
I AM THAT WHICH IS, HATH EVER BEEN, SHALL EVER BE.
THOSE ARE THE WORDS OF GOD!
SINCE THOU DOST NOT BELIEVE, SURELY THAT IS OF LITTLE IMPORT.
ARE YOU REAL?
ART THOU?
WHY AM I HERE, WHAT DO YOU WANT OF ME?
THOU HAST LIVED TOO LONG, LORD OF DUNREITH. THOU MUST LEAVE THY NEST AND FLY-- OR FALL!
RIDDLES!?!
I'VE NO PATIENCE FOR YOUR IDIOT GAMES! I'M FIGHTING FOR MY LIFE! ANSWER ME STRAIGHT, DAMN YOU -- WILL YOU HELP ME!
IS'T NOT WHAT I HAVE DONE? THE POWER IS THINE, CHILDE-- AS'T HAS BEEN SINCE BEFORE YOUR SUN BURNED HOT UPON THIS PRETTY PLACE.
ALL THOU NEED'ST DO IS SUMMON IT.

HOW?!?
THE BEAST LIED, IT MUST HAVE! I'M NO STRONGER THAN I WAS, I MOVE NO FASTER, MY WOUNDS-- WAIT!
I WAS MORTAL HURT-- DYING-- WHEN FIRST THE DRAGON APPEARED. ITS FLAME HEALED ME, MADE ME ONCE MORE WHOLE.
PERHAPS THAT ELDRITCH FIRE IS THE KEY.
IN HIS MIND'S-EYE, HE BURNS...
...AND THEN, IMAGINATION BECOMES REALITY.
MY PHYSICAL BODY-- STILL FROZEN, ENTOMBED WITHIN THE EARTH--
-- BUT THIS PHANTOM FORM CAN MOVE!
THE GHOULS ARE TERRIFIED.
I'TRUTH, SO AM I!

MY FIERY BLADE CUTS-- WHERE STEEL COULD NOT!
THESE MUST BE THE SPIRITS OF THE REVEREND SISTERS--
-- ENSLAVED, TRANSFORMED, BY THEIR SACRILIGEOUS MURDER.
YESTERDAY, I WOULD HAVE SCOFFED AT SUCH A TALE.
YET HOW CAN I DENY THE EVIDENCE OF MY OWN EYES?!
I PRAY MY SWORD RELEASES YOU FROM YOUR CURSE, GENTLE LADIES--
--AND PERMITS YOUR SOULS TO JOURNEY ONWARDS TO YOUR JUST AND EVERLASTING REPOSE.
IF THERE IS A HEAVEN, YOU'VE TRULY EARNED THEIR PLACE IN IT.
I'M-- RETURNING TO MY BODY. WHAT A STRANGE SENSATION THIS IS-- AKIN TO DONNING A SNUG JERKIN.
I FEEL AS WEARY AS AFTER A PHYSICAL BATTLE-- THE EFFORT IS EVIDENTLY THE SAME, REGARDLESS.

I'M STILL BURIED!
NO BREATH--
--NO STRENGTH-- WHICH WAY IS UP, AM I DIGGING IN THE RIGHT DIRECTION?!!

THANK GOD--
--LIGHT!

HERE, BRIAN, HE'S HERE--
--I HAVE HIM!
SAINTS BE PRAISED, HE LIVES!

AYE, JAMIE'S A TOUGH LAD, HE IS, TOO DAMN' STUBBORN TO DIE.
HIS SURCOAT AND MAIL--TORN--STAINED WITH BLOOD!
WHAT HAPPENED TO HIM, BRIAN?! WHAT PULLED HIM UNDERGROUND?!!

STRANGE--DESPITE YOUR MASTER'S RAVAGED APPEARANCE, THERE ISN'T A MARK ON HIM! HOW CAN THAT BE?!!
THE DRAGON--ITS FLAME HEALED MY WOUNDS.
WHAT DID YOU SAY, SIR JAMES?! ARE YOU WELL?!
I SHALL BE--THANKS TO YOU. I AM IN YOUR DEBT, LADY ELLIANNE.
CONSIDER OUR SCALES BALANCED, LIFE FOR LIFE.

I WAS SO AFRAID WHEN YOU VANISHED. ALL MY NURSE'S STORIES-- ALL THE FOLK TALES I'D EVER HEARD-- ABOUT GHOSTS AND DEMONS AND ACCURSED SPIRITS CAME RUSHING BACK INTO MY MIND.
YET YOU SPRANG TO MY AID. AS I SAID, ELLIANNE, YOUR COURAGE WOULD DO A BELTED KNIGHT PROUD.
YOU NEED GRIEVE NO LONGER FOR THE HOLY SISTERS. I GIVE MY WORD, THEIR TORMENT IS ENDED, THEIR SOULS FOREVER FREE.
I WANT TO TAKE HER IN MY ARMS-- HER TEARS STRIKE ME TO THE HEART--

-- IT'S LUCKY FOR BOTH OF US I'M TOO WEAK TO MOVE.
I'VE KNOWN COUNTLESS WOMEN -- THOUGHT MYSELF IN LOVE MORE THAN ONCE -- WHY DOES SHE AFFECT ME SO?!
Eh-- WHAT'S THAT?!

STAND WHERE YOU ARE!
MAKE NEITHER MOVE NOR OUTCRY--
--ON PERIL OF YOUR LIVES!

YOU'RE A LONG WAY OFF YOUR PATCH, LOCKSLEY.
IF I'M ANY JUDGE OF ACCENTS, SCOTSMAN, SO'RE YOU.
BRIAN, WHO ARE THESE MEN?!
YON HANDSOME ROGUE IS THE EARL OF HUNTINGDON. UP NOTTINGHAM WAY-- 'ROUND SHERWOOD FOREST-- HE'S BETTER KNOWN THESE DAYS AS...

ROBIN HOOD!?!
YOU'LL NOT TAKE US WITHOUT A FIGHT, RENEGADE!
LAY HAND ON ME OR MY COMPANIONS, AND MY FATHER WILL NOT REST 'TIL HE HAS SCATTERED YOUR ASHES TO THE FOUR WINDS!

PEACE, MILADY! PUT UP YOUR BLADE, WE'VE NOTHING TO FEAR!
YOU DARE CALL THIS VILLAIN, FRIEND?!
I GIVE EACH MAN-- AND MAID-- THEIR PROPER DUE. WHATEVER HE'S CALLED-- BY THOSE WI' CAUSE TO HATE HIM-- ROB'S NOTHING LIKE THE SCUM WHO AMBUSHED YOU.

MY THANKS FOR YOUR KIND WORDS, SIR.
BELIEVE NOT OUR REPUTATION, GENTLE LADY.
WE PREY SOLELY ON THOSE WHO OPPRESS THE WEAK AND HELPLESS. THE RICHES WE SEIZE, WE GIVE TO THE POOR.

AM I WRONG, SIR KNIGHT, OR DO I ADDRESS THE LEGENDARY BLACK DRAGON OF CA'RYNTH?
I'M DUNREITH.
WELCOME HOME, MILORD. ASK OF US ANYTHING, WE ARE YOURS TO COMMAND.

LATER...
IT'S DONE.
THANK YOU.
A BAD BUSINESS, THIS. FRIAR TUCK IS SPEAKING THE LAST RITES. WHEN HE'S FINISHED, WE'LL GIVE THE LADIES AND THEIR PRIEST A PROPER BURIEL IN THE FIELD BY THE ABBEY.
I THOUGHT I'D SEEN ALL MANNER OF HORROR-- BY THE ETERNAL, WHAT PURPOSE DID SUCH BLASPHEMY SERVE?

YOU JUST SAID IT: BLASPHEMY. A DELIBERATE-- AND PROBABLY SUCCESSFUL-- ATTEMPT TO DESECRATE THIS ANCIENT SEAT OF POWER...
...NOT ONLY IN TERMS OF THE OLD FAITH, BUT THE NEW.

TO WHAT END?
I DON'T KNOW.
WHO DID THIS, WHO'S RESPONSIBLE?!
THAT, MY FRIEND, IS WHAT I'M HERE TO LEARN.

IT'S SAID YOU'RE A SORCERER.
MEANING--?
AS MUCH AS YOU'RE A WOLFSHEAD OUTLAW, MASTER BOWMAN.

WE BOTH OF US WALK BETWEEN SHADOW AND LIGHT, ROBIN. WHO AND WHAT WE ARE IS A QUESTION FAR MORE EASILY ASKED THAN ANSWERED.
IF YOU'LL EXCUSE ME, I'VE A GREAT DEAL TO CONSIDER.

BY GOD AN' GODDESS BOTH, JAMIE, I WISH I HAD THE MEANS TO EASE YOUR PAIN...
... AN' THE COURAGE TO CALL LADY ELLIANNE AWAY.
WHO CAN SAY, P'RHAPS IT'S F'R THE BEST I DON'T.
SHE FOUND YOU, WITHIN THE SARCEN CIRCLE, WHEN I COULD NOT.

"MAYHAP SHE DOES KNOW YUIR HEART BETTER THAN I."
MY FIRST ENCOUNTER WITH THE DRAGON, I COULD-- AND DID-- PASS OFF AS AN HALLUCINATION, A FEVER DREAM BROUGHT ON BY MY WOUNDS.
EXCEPT THAT NOWISE DID THAT EXPLAIN MY MIRACULOUS RECOVERY.
WHAT IN HELL DO I TELL MYSELF NOW?!

I DIDN'T STUMBLE INTO QUICKSAND-- AFTER ELLIANNE PULLED ME LOOSE, THE GROUND WAS FIRM AS ROCK.
THOSE WEREN'T PHANTOMS WHO TORE MY ARMOR, MY CLOTHES-- MY... FLESH. IF THE GHOULS WERE REAL, THE DRAGON MUST BE, TOO.
THERE'S A WICKED IRONY.

ALL MY DAYS, I'VE SECRETLY SCOFFED AT THE TALES OF DUNREITH THE MAGE--*I* KNEW BETTER: THAT IT WAS NOT, COULD NOT, BE SO.
AT THE SAME TIME, I WASN'T ABOVE USING THAT NOTORIETY TO MY OWN ADVANTAGE WHEN THE NEED AROSE.
HERE I AM, THEN, SEEMINGLY HOIST ON MY OWN PETARD, TRAPPED BY MY OWN FRAUD AND DECEPTION.

ELEANOR TURNED TO ME, IN HOPES MY SUPPOSED SKILLS COULD COUNTER WHATEVER EVIL WAS AFOOT IN THE WESTLANDS. THE TRAGEDY IS, THOSE MALEFIC FORCES ARE REAL-- MAGIC IS **REAL**--
-- WHEREAS THE QUEEN'S CHAMPION IS ONLY A MAN, WHO HASN'T THE SLIGHTEST NOTION OF HOW TO COMBAT THEM.
JAMIE...?
ELLIANNE!
FORGIVE ME! I WAS SO LOST IN THOUGHT I DIDN'T HEAR YOUR APPROACH.

THE FAULT IS MINE FOR DISTURBING YOU.
IS ANYTHING THE MATTER?
I... DIDN'T WANT TO BE ALONE, THAT'S ALL.
NO FEAR OF THAT, SURROUNDED BY A SCORE OF STOUT YEOMAN.
THEY COULD BE ALL THE PEOPLES OF THE WORLD, MY LORD, AND IF ONE SPECIAL SOUL WERE NOT AMONG THEM...

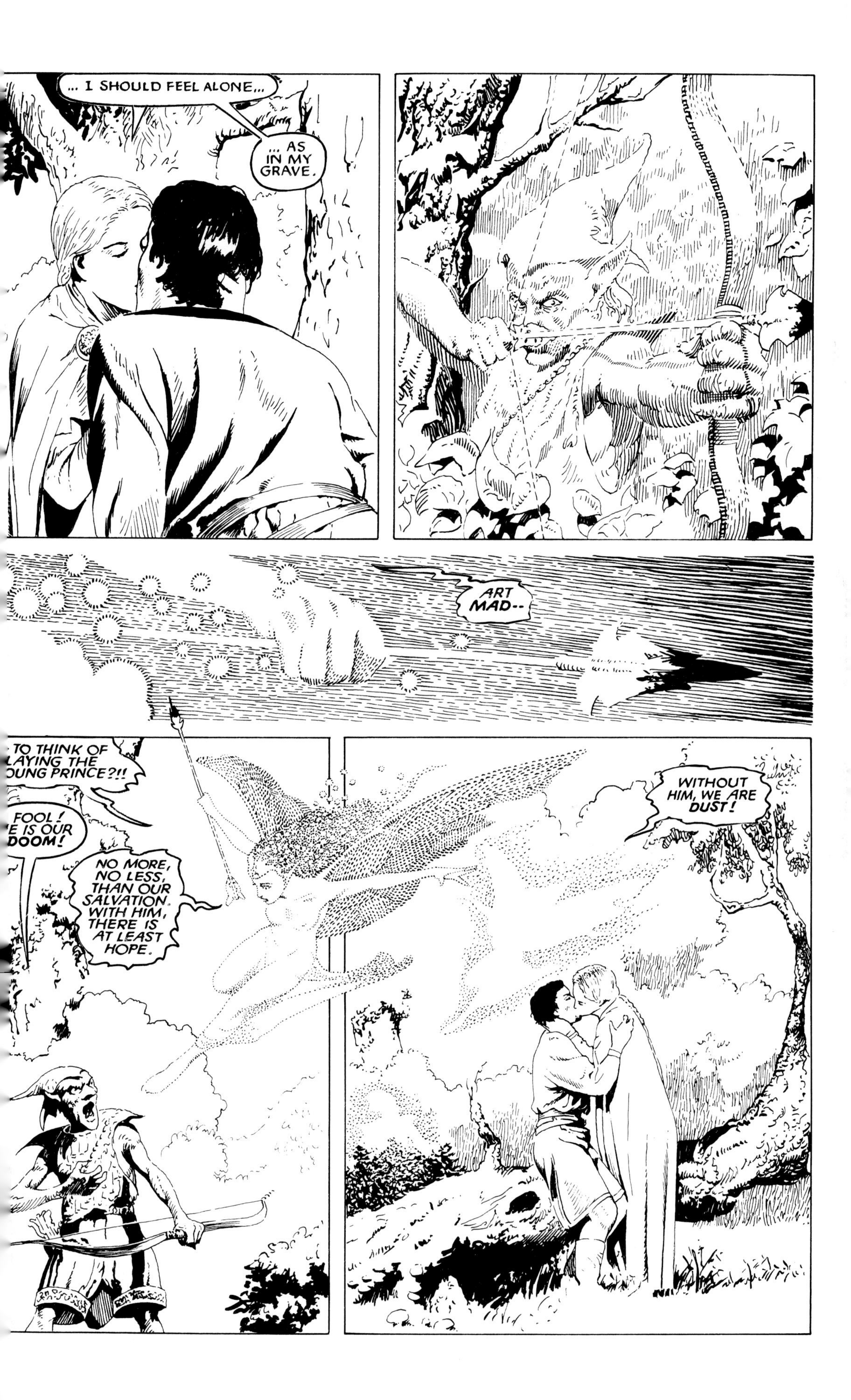
... I SHOULD FEEL ALONE...
... AS IN MY GRAVE.
ART MAD--
TO THINK OF LAYING THE OUNG PRINCE?!!
FOOL! E IS OUR DOOM!
NO MORE, NO LESS, THAN OUR SALVATION. WITH HIM, THERE IS AT LEAST HOPE.
WITHOUT HIM, WE ARE DUST!

LATER STILL...
WHAT BROUGHT YOU TO GLENOWYN, ROB?
THE SAME, I'LL WAGER, AS YOU.
CHRISTMAS PAST, THESE ATTACKS BEGAN-- THE FIRST ON THE WINTER SOLSTICE-- RANGING THE LENGTH OF THE WELSH BORDER COUNTRY, TO THE FRINGES OF SHERWOOD ITSELF!
SINCE THE VICTIMS WERE MOSTLY PEASANT AND SAXON-- THE INITIAL DESECRATIONS SOLELY OF "PAGAN" SHRINES-- THE NOBILITY TURNED A BLIND EYE. NOT A FEW CALLED IT THE LORD'S GOOD WORK. BUT THE ATROCITIES HAVE BEEN STEADILY INCREASING, IN NUMBER AND SEVERITY.

NORMAN BLOOD'S BEEN SPILLED, CHRISTIAN CHURCHES DEFILED-- TOO MUCH AT LONG LAST TO IGNORE.
ONLY ONE SHIRE'S BEEN SPARED-- **GLENOWYN.** I THOUGHT THAT BORE INVESTIGATION.

LEAVE THAT TASK TO ME.
I WANT YOU TO RAISE AN ARMY-- EVERY ABLE-BODIED MAN, WOMAN AND CHILD WITHIN TWO DAYS' MARCH OF EDMUND'S CASTLE, READY TO MARCH AT A MOMENT'S NOTICE.
I LEAD A BAND OF OUTLAWS, DUNREITH--WOULDN'T IT BE BETTER TO SUMMON ROYAL TROOPS?

THEY'D BE TOO LITTLE AND PROBABLY TOO LATE. I SPEAK FOR THE CROWN, LOCKSLEY, AND ACT FOR THE SAKE OF THE *REALM*-- WILL YOU DENY THAT CALL?!
I'LL DO WHAT I CAN.

BUT IT'D HELP TO KNOW THE TRUTH O' THIS. WHAT'S HAPPENING, WHAT ARE WE FACING-- IS IT HONEST REBELLION, OR... SOMETHING MORE?!
I WISH I KNEW...
...AND PRAY I NEVER LEAR

THE FOLLOWING DAY...
GLENOWYN'S A FAIR-SIZED TOWN AN' MIGHTILY PROSPEROUS BY THE LOOK OF IT. YUIR DA'S DONE WELL FOR HIMSELF, LASS.
ARE ALL HIGHLAND SQUIRES AS FREE-TONGUED AS YOU, MASTER GRIFFON?
AYE. WE'RE A CUSSEDLY INDEPENDENT LOT, MORE STIFF-NECKED I'LL HAZARD THAN E'EN THESE LEEK-EATING WELSHMEN.
GOOD-NESS!
I MEAN NO OFFENSE.
REST ASSURED, NONE IS TAKEN. BUT MY FATHER AND HIS SERVANTS MAY NOT BE AS FORGIVING.
SOME OF THIS HOLDING, THE EARL INHERITED; SOME CAME WITH MY LATE MOTHER-- REST HER SOUL--AS HER DOWRY; SOME WAS REWARD FOR LOYAL SERVICE TO KING HENRY. FATHER'S RULED IT WELL...
MORE USTLY AND AIRLY THAN ANY I'VE NOWN.
THE CASTLE'S A BIT FARTHER ON.
THEN, I'LL TAKE MY LEAVE AN' IT PLEASE YOU, SIR-- TO FIND US LODGING. AS THE LADY SAID, IT WOULDN'T DO F'R ME T' PUT A FOOT WRONG B'FORE QUALITY FOLK AN' SPOIL HER HOMECOMING.
AFTER ALL WE'VE ENDURED, I SHOULDN'T FEEL SO EXCITED-- EVEN HAPPY-- BUT I DO!
I'D BE THE SAME.
WILL YOU BE LEAVING THEN, TO RIDE NORTH TO CA'RYNTH?
HEN MY ASK IS OMPLETE.
BRI'LL SCOUT THE TAVERNS, TAKE HEED OF LOCAL GOSSIP-- UNLESS SOMETHING BREAKS SOONER, WE'LL RENDEZVOUS IN A DAY OR SO TO COMPARE NOTES.
THE ROAD'S UNUSUALLY CROWDED-- ALL MANNER OF GENTRY FLOCKING TOWARDS THE CASTLE.

YOUR PARDON, SIR KNIGHT-- WHAT'S THE OCCASION?
A TOURNAMENT, FRIEND, HOSTED BY THE EARL AND HIS SISTER, THE LADY ANNE!
EVERY NOBLE FAMILY IN THE WEST WILL BE HERE, SPORTING THEIR FINEST SILKS AND GOWNS-- WHILE THE EARL'S ONLY CHILD LOOKS NO BETTER THAN A COMMON RAGAMUFFIN.
HARDLY "COMMON."
THIS IS NO LAUGHING MATTER! MY FATHER WILL BE SO ASHAMED--!
YOU JUDGE EDMUND-- AND YOURSELF--TOO HARSHLY.
JAMIE-- LET'S TURN AWAY WHILE WE STILL CAN! TAKE ME WITH YOU AND BRIAN TO YOUR HIGHLANDS!
I'D GIVE MY SOUL TO SAY, "YES." I'VE NEVER WANTED ANYTHING MORE.
BUT I GAVE MY WORD TO THE QUEEN.
IT'S TOO LATE, LITTLE ONE--
-- WE'VE ARRIVED.

ROTHER--
BEHOLD!
Hmnh?
THAT CASTLE'S A MASTERPIECE! NO DOUBT AS WELL MANNED AND PROVISIONED AS IT IS WELL-BUILT. ONLY A LUNATIC WOULD ATTEMPT TO SEIZE BY STORM OR SEIGE.
CHIN HIGH--THE GORGONS AWAIT!
STOP IT, JAMIE!
YOU MUSTN'T MAKE ME LAUGH, NOT NOW!
THERE HE IS--MY FATHER!"
CAN IT BE?!
BY ALL THE APOSTLES IN HELL, IT IS!
JAMES DUNREITH!
EDMUND!
HE'S YOUNGER THAN I, YET HE LOOKS SO OLD!
THE YEARS HAVE BEEN KIND TO YOU, MY LORD EARL.
I'D FEW
MPLAINTS,
Y LORD
UKE, 'TIL I
AW YOU!
YOU'VE NOT AGED A DAY, YOU SCOUNDREL, IN OVER TWENTY YEARS!
I NEVER REALIZED--BUT THAT'S TRUE!
SEE, ANNIE, WHO'S BROUGHT OUR PRECIOUS ELLIANNE HOME-- MY DEAREST COMRADE! AND JAMIE, ALLOW ME TO PRESENT MY SISTER, THE LADY ANNE GLENOWYN.
IS THIS THE LATEST FASHION AT COURT?
Uh, NO, MILADY, THAT IS, I...
YOU NEEDN'T BLUSH, CHILD, I QUITE UNDERSTAND.
COME, WE'LL SOON HAVE YOU BATHED AND GOWNED AND PROPERLY SEEN TO, AS BEFITS A DAUGHTER OF GLENOWYN.
IT IS GOOD TO HAVE YOU HOME, ELLI.
I'M AS HAPPY TO BE HERE.

IS'T TRUE YOU'VE TRAVELLED THE LENGTH OF THE SILK ROAD, TO FABLED CATHAY?
AND THE ISLANDS BEYOND.
BY THE ETERNAL, I'D'VE GIVEN MUCH TO SEE THAT BY YOUR SIDE. HENRY WAS WRONG TO BANISH YOU, JAMIE...
...AND I WAS WRONG TO LET YOU GO ALONE.

TELL ME, HOW CAME YOU TO RIDE WITH ELLIANNE? WHERE'S HER COMPANION, THAT DeLACEY GIRL--AND CAPTAIN MORRIS, WHOM I SENT TO ESCORT THEM BOTH?
I'M SORRY, EDMUND, I'VE SAD NEWS. LADY ISABEL, YOUR OFFICER AND MEN WERE SLAIN...
I WARNED YOU, DOG--

--WHAT WOULD HAPPEN SHOULD E'ER AGAIN YOU CROSS MY PATH!
BURGO!
HOW DARE YOU?! THIS MAN IS MY GUEST!!

WHERE DID THAT COME FROM?! I MISJUDGED THE BOY--WHEN WE MET AT THE INN, HE SEEMED THE SORT WHO'D ONLY CHALLEN THOSE FAR WEAKER THAN HIMSEL
DAMN! I WANT NO TROUBLE, BUT THIS PUBLIC INSULT LEAVES ME LITTLE ALTERNATIVE.

JAMES, WHAT SAY YOU?!
MUCH AS I'D WISH DIFFERENT, HONOR DEMANDS SATISFACTION.
SO BE IT! YOU'LL MEET TOMORROW, AS PART OF THE TOURNEY--WITH PADDED LANCES, MIND YOU, I WANT NO BLOOD SPILLED!
'TIL THEN, BURGO FITZWARREN, YOU MAKE YOURSELF SCARCE! AND AFTER-WARDS, SIRRAH, YOU WILL HAVE TO DEAL WITH ME!

FORGIVE ME, JAMIE, THIS ISN'T AT ALL THE WELCOME YOU DESERVE.
MOST HOLY BLESSED VIRGIN--HARRY, WHAT HAVE I DONE?!
WHAT HAVE I DONE?!!

THAT NIGHT...

DEAR, LOVELY, DECEITFUL ANNE--
--WHAT, PRAY TELL, ARE YOU PLAYING AT?!
EDMUND--?!!

YOU NOW NOUGH ASK, MY ORD...
...WHAT NEED HAVE I TO ANSWER?

YOU SENT THE BRIGANDS TO MASSACRE ELLIANNE'S TRAIN. I SAID NOTHING EARLIER, BECAUSE THE PLOY FAILED. THE GIRL SURVIVED.
BUT PROMPTING THAT POPPINJAY TO STRIKE DUNREITH-- ANNE, YOU GO TOO FAR.
GOOD. THERE MAY YET BE WORSE TO COME.
YOU'RE HURTING ME, EDMUND.
DO YOU PLAN TO AID BURGO, DEAR SISTER, IN TOMORROW'S JOUST-- THE SAME WAY YOU PROVOKED HIM-- WITH YOUR *MAGICKS?!*

NO ANSWER.
SUCH SILENCE ILL BECOMES YOU. HAS YOUR VAUNTED COURAGE FLED?
ELLIANNE IS MY CHILD, EDMUND! I'D RATHER SEE HER DEAD THAN DAMNED!
YOU THINK I FEEL ANY DIFFERENT?! JAMES DUNREITH IS MY DEAREST FRIEND!
HE ALONE ACCEPTED ME WHEN FIRST I CAME TO COURT, HE STOOD BY ME-- WE WERE AS BROTHERS-- BY THE CHRIST, I LOVE HIM, ANNE, AS I NEVER HAVE ANY WOMAN!
YET-- TO DO WHAT MUST BE DONE TO CLEANSE THIS LAND-- I WILL GLADL SACRIFICE HIM!

WE MUST EACH LOSE THAT WHICH WE HOLD MOST DEAR. WE ACCEPTED THAT FROM THE START.
I... DID NOT THINK THEN IT WOULD BE SO HARD--
--NOR HURT SO MUCH.
THAT IS WHAT GIVES THE SPELL ITS FEARSOME POTENCY; ITS FORCE IS TORN FROM OUR VERY HEARTS AND SOULS.
VICTORY IS WITHIN OUR GRASP, MY LOVE. IT IS TOO LATE TO TURN BACK.

FOR BRITAIN'S SAKE, WE MUST BE STRONG!
AGAINST ALL ODDS-- AGAINST THE MIGHT AND MAJESTY OF HEAVEN ITSELF-- WE WILL PREVAIL!

COME FOR ME, JAMIE--
-- IF YOU DARE!
JOHN BOLTON ©

THA'S IT, M'LUD--COO, WHAT A BLOW!
THE EARL IS ONE OF THE FINEST SWORDSMEN IN ENGLAND--YET JAMES DUNREITH MATCHES HIM STROKE FOR STROKE!
YOU'VE YOUR WORK CUT OUT FOR YOU THIS AFTERNOON, BURGO MY LAD!
MIGHT HAVE BEEN A WEE BIT HASTY, *HMNH*, CHALLENGING YON SCOTS BUMPKIN TO A DUEL?
AN' HE'S--*hic*--THE EARL'S **FRIEND**, TO BOOT! YOU KNOW THAT ARROGANT--*hic*--HALF-BREED PIG-BASTARD HATES US NORMANS. HE'LL NE'ER FORGIVE YOU SHOULD YOU WIN.
SMALL CHANCE OF THAT, BY THE LOOK OF THINGS.
BUT FOR GOD'S SAKE RANULF, KEEP YOUR VOICE DOWN--LEST DeVALERE HEAR YOU!

JUST LIKE OLD TIMES, eh, JAMIE?!
THE YEARS HAVEN'T DULLED YOUR EDGE.
NOR YOURS, MY LORD EDMUND!

LADY ANNE--IN THE COURTYARD--
--MY FATHER AND SIR JAMES!

HEY'VE
EEN AT
SINCE
UNRISE.
HARDLY LIKELY, WITH PADDED SURCOATS AND BLUNT STEEL.
I FEEL ASHAMED-- A LOYAL DAUGHTER SHOULD CHEER ON HER SIRE, YET I PRAY NO HARM COMES TO MY LORD DUNREITH, EITHER.

COME ALONG, CHILD-- INTO THE TUB BEFORE YOU CATCH A CHILL-- YOU'LL HAVE OPPORTUNITIES A'PLENTY TO SEE YOUR PALADIN AT THE TOURNEY, IN ALL HIS KNIGHTLY GLORY.
AND WHEN THAT MOMENT COMES, YOU'LL GREET HIM AS A PROPER LADY, THE PROUD DAUGHTER OF A NOBLE HOUSE--
--NOT SOME RAGAMUFFIN OF THE ROAD.

IDN'T THEY
EACH YOU
NYTHING
QUEEN
LEANOR'S
OUSE-
HOLD?!
TO READ AND WRITE, TO RIDE AND HUNT, TO DEFEND MYSELF AND, MOST IMPORTANTLY, HER MAJESTY SAID, TO THINK.
SKILLS I'M NOT LIKELY TO NEED AS THE BRIDE OF SOME COUNTRY BARON.
MY LADY, WHY ARE YOU BATHING ME? I REALLY NEED NO HELP...

I RAISED YOU, ELLIANNE-- I HAVE NOT SEEN YOU SINCE YOU BECAME A ROYAL WARD IN CHILDHOOD-- WOULD YOU DENY ME SO SIMPLE A PLEASURE...
...SO SMALL A GESTURE OF MY LOVE?
FORGIVE ME, I-- OWW!

WHAT'S THE MATTER?
MY CRUCIFIX-- IT'S GOTTEN TANGLED IN MY HAIR. STRANGE, THAT'S NEVER HAPPENED BEFORE.
GIVE IT TO ME, LASS. I'LL SET IT ASIDE FOR SAFEKEEPING.

SO, ELLI, YOU FOLLOW THE PATH OF THE *ONE GOD?*
OF COURSE.
IN THIS WILD COUNTRY...

...NOT EVERYONE DOES.
THANK CHRIST TODAY'S WILL BE A FRIENDLY JOUST. THE WORST I RISK ARE SOME BRUISES AND CRACKED BONES.
BUT THOSE TWO-- EVEN THOUGH THIS IS PRACTICE, THEY SEEM TO BE FIGHTING FOR REAL, GIVING ALL THEY HAVE!

GOT YOU, DUNREITH!

DO YOU YIELD, SIR KNIGHT...
...OR MUST I SEND YOU TO YOUR JUST REWARD?
MY LIFE, EDMUND, IS AS EVER YOURS.
I'M GLAD YO REMEMBERE SOMEDAY I'LL HOLD YOU TO THAT.

VHAT MADNESS IS THIS?! THEY SPOKE N JEST, YET I'M CERTAIN -- HAD UNREITH NOT SURRENDERED -- LORD DMUND WOULD HAVE RUN HIM THROUGH!
THINK YOU CAN TAKE THE SCOT -- *hic* -- BURGO?
F A ALF-REED ORMAN AN, ANULF... I CAN WITH EASE.
I MAY HAVE SEEN MY SHARE OF WINTERS, JAMIE -- WITH SNOW ENOUGH IN MY HAIR TO PROVE IT --
-- BUT I'VE YET TO MEET MY MATCH!
I CONCEDE, EDMUND, YOU'RE AS FAST AND STRONG AS EVER. MOST IMPRESSIVE.
I'M ALSO SLY AS THE DEVIL -- WHICH I LEARNED FROM OUR LATE KING HENRY -- THAT, ABOVE ALL ELSE, IS WHY I LIVE AND PROSPER IN A LAND FILLED TO OVERFLOWING WITH MY ENEMIES.
BUT ENOUGH OF POLITICS -- IT'S TOO EARLY IN THE DAY FOR THIS!
THIS WORKOUT'S GIVEN ME AN APPETITE! SO, IN, MY LORD OF CA'RYNTH, TO A WELL-EARNED BREAKFAST! I WANT TO HEAR MORE OF YOUR TRAVELS. IS'T TRUE, ABOUT THE WENCHES OF CATHAY --?!!
DU HAVE YOUR FATHER'S HAIR -- RIGHT AND GOLDEN AS A MIDSUMMER SUN.
BUT YOUR MOTHER'S EYES.
WHAT'S THAT --?!
THE TAPESTRY STIRRED -- SOMEONE'S WATCHING!
I NEVER KNEW HER. SHE DIED, I'M TOLD, IN CHILDBIRTH --
MILADY -- I DIDN'T REALIZE -- MY TIME OF THE MONTH -- I'M SORRY, I'M BLEEDING. I'VE STAINED YOUR ROBE -- !
IS THAT ALL? I THOUGHT IT WAS SOMETHING SERIOUS.

BUT THE SILK-- IT'S RUINED!
THESE THINGS HAPPEN-- THE PRICE WE PAY FOR BEING WOMEN.
I'LL RINSE THE STAIN BEFORE IT SETS, WHILE YOU FINISH DRESSING. ANYTHING YOU REQUIRE, SIMPLY ASK YOUR MAIDS. I'LL BE ALONG DIRECTLY.

I SHOULD BURN THIS-- BUT TO WHAT END? ONE WAY OR ANOTHER, EDMUND WILL GET WHAT HE NEEDS.
AND TRAMPLE ANY WHO STAND IN HIS WAY.
GOOD MORROW, BROTHER.

MY LADY SISTER, YOU LOOK WELL.
THE TOWER-- AND OUR WORK AWAIT, ANNE.
SHALL WE--?

WHY SO UPSET, MY DEAR?
I DISLIKE SPIES, ESPECIALLY IN MY CHAMBERS. WERE YOU CONCERNED I'D SLIT THE GIRL'S THROAT, EDMUND, OR DROWN HER IN HER TUB?
NEITHER. I MERELY SENSED THE FLOW OF BLOOD-- YOU KNOW AS WELL AS I, ANNE, THAT OUR ENCHANTMENTS ARE BEST CAST WHEN IT IS FRESH.

BESIDES, WHERE IS THE HARM IN A FATHER LOOKING IN ON HIS ONLY CHILD?
BASTARD!

BASTARD!
HOW DARE YOU SPEAK THUS OF HER, HOW DARE YOU MOCK ME!?!

HE *ISN'T* OURS-- NOT HE SLIGHTEST ART OF HER YOURS-- HE'S *MINE!*
MY FLESH, MY BLOOD, *MY DAUGHTER!*
AND SHE'LL DIE-- BY MY HAND-- WITHOUT EVER KNOWING!

EVERY SPELL HAS ITS PRICE, MY HEART-- AND WHAT WE PLAN DEMANDS THE SACRIFICE OF THAT WHICH WE HOLD MOST PRECIOUS.
FROM YOU, YOUR BABE. FROM ME...
... MY BELOVED.
JAMIE WILL NEVER KNOW, EITHER, WHO HE IS AND WHAT HE MEANS TO ME.

HIS IS AS HARD FOR ME S YOU, ANNE-- NEVER LIEVE DIFFERENT--
-- BUT IT MUST BE DONE, IF OUR LAND AND OUR PEOPLE ARE TO BE *FREE!*
SWEET WORDS.
THEY ALMOST MAKE ME BELIEVE YOU.

I NEVER SHOULD HAVE TAUGHT YOU THE ANCIENT ARTS.
BUT YOU DID.

EDMUND--
--INTRUDERS!
THE MAGI, SISTER--
--FLEE!

NOT SO FAST, PRETTILINGS!
AAYAIFEEEE!
WHAT'S THAT?!

COULD HAVE
VORN I HEARD
SCREAM-- AND
W A FLASH,
RIGHT AS LIGHTNING,
EN AGAINST A
UNLIT SKY.
BUT EVERYONE ELSE ACTS AS IF NOTHING UNTOWARD HAS HAPPENED.
IT MUST BE MY IMAGINATION. WHO'S THERE--? *ELLIANNE!*
I WAS DREAMING-- WHAT OTHER EXPLANATION IS THERE? THE KEEP IS AS STILL AND QUIET AS CAN BE.
JAMIE?! I WONDER WHERE HE'S RIDING?
AVE GO
Y REINS,
R BURGO,
YOU
LEASE.
AND IF I DO NOT?
I TRUST, SIR JAMES, THIS ISN'T THE LAST WE'LL SEE OF YOU. NOT LOST YOUR FABLED COURAGE, I HOPE.
AFTER ALL, YOU'RE EXPECTED TO FACE ME IN THE LISTS, AND I WOULD DEARLY HATE TO BE DISAPPOINTED.
I'LL BE THERE.
GOOD.
I JUST WANTED TO BE SURE.
ART AFEAR'D, SMALLING?
BE NOT SO, FOR DEATH SHALT NE'ER CLAIM THEE, AT MY HAND.

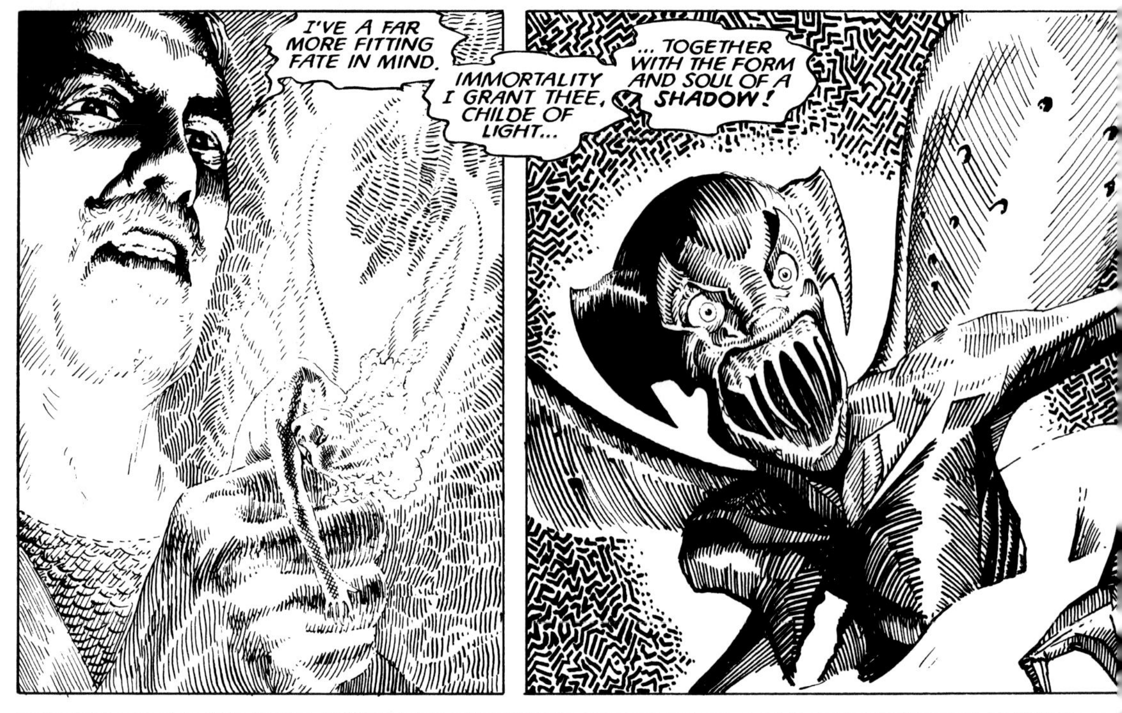
I'VE A FAR MORE FITTING FATE IN MIND.
IMMORTALITY I GRANT THEE, CHILDE OF LIGHT...
...TOGETHER WITH THE FORM AND SOUL OF A SHADOW!

FOLLOW MY LOVE, MY SERVANT-- RELATE TO ME WHERE HE GOES, WHO HE SEES, WHAT HE SAYS AND DOES.

THE SHAPE OF THINGS TO COME--MAGNIFICENT!
IT DOESN'T ALARM YOU, WHAT THEY MAY HAVE LEARNED.
ONLY ONE FORCE IN THE REALM CAN POSSIBLY EQUAL ME, ANNE, AND HE IS COMPLETELY IN MY POWER.
THERE'S STILL THE TOURNEY.

YOU CONSIDER BURGO FITZWARREN A MATCH FOR DUNREITH?! ANNE, MY DARLING ANNE, I DO SO ADORE YOUR SENSE OF HUMOR!
FROM WHENCE COMES SUCH RESPECT? YOU BEAT HIM HANDILY THIS MORNING.

JAMES CARES NOTHING FOR PRACTI
DUELS-- WIN OR LOSE, IT'S THE SAM
TO HIM. BUT WITH HIS LIFE AT HAZAR
HE'S A DIFFERENT MAN-- AND THE
DEADLIEST WARRIOR I'VE EVER KNOW
PLAY YOUR GAMBIT, ANNE, IF YOU
MUST-- BUT MAKE NO MISTAKE-- IN
TRYING TO SAVE ELLI...
...YOU'LL MERELY CONDEMN THAT FOOLISH BOY TO CERTAIN DEATH.

HO, MASTER ARCHER!

DIDST THOU E'ER STOP T' THINK, THOU LIVING LUMP, THAT MY OAKS DON'T MUCH LIKE THEE POKIN' HOLES IN 'EM?!
CAREFUL, EAMONN!
THA' SHAFT'S TIPPED WI' STEEL, 'TIS FATAL T' YUIR KIND!
AYE-- KNOW THAT, I DID.

MADE IT MORE FUN, 'EY!
A FINE, WARM MORNING, THIS-- GIVES A SOUL A WICKED THIRST!
Aha-- AS EVER, BRIAN, THOU'RE A MOST GENEROUS, CONSIDERATE HOST.
YOU'RE LATE, MILORD.

BUSY, WE BEEN-- GOOD WINE, THIS-- FRENCH, IS'T?
LOT O' TROUBLE HERE'BOUTS, A BAD WIND RISING, HARD DAYS AHEAD.
THE CHILDREN WEEP, THEIR GREEN FADES.
LONGAWAYS FROM HOME YOU ARE, GRIFFON.

THE DRAGON CALLED.
Phaugggh!
WHATEVER YOU FEEL, EAMONN, WHATE'ER YOU BELIEVE, THE DRAGON IS MY LIEGE LORD. I'LL HEAR NO ONE DEFAME OR GAINSAY HIM, NOT EVEN A PRINCE OF THE SIDHE!

FORGIVE ME, LAD. MY SPEECH WAS INTEMPERATE -- THOUGH I'LL NOT DENY THE THOUGHT THAT SPAWNED 'EM.
THE DRAGON'S POWER IN EVIL HANDS IS A WEAPON BEYOND COMPREHENSION-- THOU'RT HUMAN, BRIAN, THOU HAST NO IDEA -- THE LAND WOULD BE LAID WASTE FOREVER.
FOREVER, GRIFFON-- FOR AS LONG AS THE WORLD SPINS AN' THE SUN BURNS AMONG'ST THE STARS!

A MISTAKE MADE HERE, BY US, COULD SPAWN A MALIGNANCY THAT'LL CORRUPT THE EARTH AN' ALL WHO LIVE ON'T!
I KNOW, EAMONN-- BUT JAMIE IS MY FRIEND!

MORE FOOL THOU.
THY FLASK IS EMPTY, HAST ANY--?!
EAMONNNNNN
WHAT-- ?!!

ONE OF THE FAIRY FOLK!
MIÈRÉ!?!

MERCIFUL GODDESS--!?!
URSED, SHE
S--ACCURSED!
EAMONN--
YUIR
HAND?!!
UR LADY SMILES ON ME THIS DAY-- A NEAR THING, IT WAS,
BUT I MANAGED TO CHECK THE MALEFIC ENCHANTMENT.
THOSE FLAMES WERE HER SACRED FIRE-- USED 'EM, I DID, TO CLEANSE MY FLESH O' THAT FOUL CONTAGION. IN ALL MY SEASONS, GRIFFON, I'VE NE'ER FELT ANYTHING SO VILE!
LOOK NOT SO STRICKEN, BOY. ALREADY, I HEAL-- BY SOLSTICE, I'LL BE WHOLE ONCE AGAIN.
WOULD I COULD SAY THE SAME FOR MY CHILDE.
SHE BREATHES, EAMONN-- SHE YET LIVES!
LIE-- THE CRUELEST OF ECEPTIONS-- SHE CARRIES WITHIN HER PLAGUE, THE EATH FOR ALL OUR FOLK!
HY HUMANITY PROTECTS THEE, GRIFFON. THOU ANST TOUCH MY GIRL WHERE I DARE NOT--SEE?!
THE PROOF OF WHAT I SPOKE BEFORE! IMAGINE THE POWER OF THE DRAGON-- THE SOUL OF THE LAND ITSELF-- IN THE HAND OF ONE WHO COULD DO THAT!
SENT THEM, I DID, TO SPY ON EDMUND-- MIÈRE AND SHÉNAI, MY PRETTY LASSES.
SHIELDED THEM WITH OUR STRONGEST MAGICKS, SWORE ONLY COLD IRON COULD HARM THEM.
WRONG, I WAS.
DAMNED, THEY ARE!

BRIAN?!
WHERE ARE YOU, MAN-- BRIAN?!!
MY SWEETING'S MISERY, GRIFFON, THOU MUST END.

WAIT--?! EAMONN, STAY!
'TIS NOT THE PROPER PLACE NOR TIME.
I BEG THEE, BRIAN-- PUT STEEL IN THY HEART AND HAND, AND STRIKE!
MEET, AND TALK AGAIN, SHALL WE-- WHEN THE MOON IS FULL AND HIGH!
FARE THEE WELL, SON OF MAN.

AND YOU, FATHER OF THE MYSTERIES.

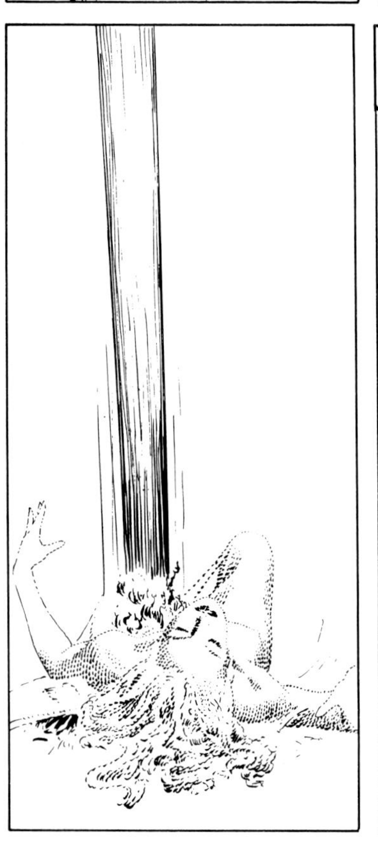

WHAT HAVE YOU THERE?
A POOR, WEE THING...
... WHO DESERVED BETTER.

WHAT'S HAPPENING, BRIAN-- TO ME, TO THE WORLD-- HAVE WE ALL GONE MAD?!
FOR THE ANSWER, MY GRACIOUS LORD, YOU'VE BUT TO LOOK WI'IN YUIRSELF.
I HAVE-- AND FOUND A DRAGON-- A FANTASTIC GREAT BEAST THAT SPOKE TO ME, IN RIDDLES! IF THAT ISN'T MADNESS...
JAMIE, LISTEN T' ME-- FOR YUIR SOUL'S SAKE BELIEVE-- THAT DRAGON IS YOU!

ROT!
BECAUSE IT ISN'T REAL!
WHY D'YOU FIND IT SO HARD TO ACCEPT?
IT CAN'T BE SEEN NOR TOUCHED NOR FELT, IT DOES NOT EXIST-- SAVE PERHAPS AS THE PHANTOM IMAGININGS OF A POOR, DEMENTED MIND!
THINK YOU SO LITTLE OF YUIRSELF?
ALL RIGHT, THEN-- EXPLAIN THIS!
A TRICK!
AWAY WITH IT--
JAMIE-- FOR GODDESS' SAKE!?!
-- AND YOU!
CAN DENY
JIRSELF NO
ONGER, JAMIE--
HERE'S NO MORE
ACE TO HIDE,
WITHIN OR WITH-
UT-- TOO MUCH AT STAKE!
RUNNING WON'T SAVE YOU!
JAMIE! YUIR FEAR WILL DOOM ALL YOU HOLD MOST DEAR!
JAMIE!?!

THAT AFTERNOON...
...IN THE TILTING GROUND BELOW GLENOWYN CASTLE...

I'VE NEVER STRUCK BRIAN IN ANGER-- YET AT THAT MOMENT, IN MY RAGE, I'D HAVE CHEERFULLY KILLED HIM.
WAS THAT WHY I FLED?
OR WAS IT FEAR...

...THAT HE SPOKE THE TRUTH?
HE HELD A FAIRY IN HIS HANDS-- BUT THEY ARE THE STUFF OF LEGEND. HOW-- ?!!
GOOD DAY AND HEALTH UNTO MY GRACIOUS LORD.
MY LADY IS MOST KIND-- ELLIANNE?! IS IT YOU?!?

AM I SO SAD A SIGHT...
...THAT YOU ONLY KNOW ME DRESSED AS SQUIRE INSTEAD OF WOMAN?
JAMIE, I WAS TEASING. YOU'RE MEANT TO SMILE-- IS SOMETHING TROUBLING YOU, SIR KNIGHT?

IT'S NOTHING. I'M MERELY PREOCCUPIED WITH THE JOUST.
WHERE'S BRIAN, SHOULDN'T HE BE ARMING YOU?
I DON'T OWN THE MAN, ELLI-- HE'S FREE TO RIDE WHERE HE PLEASES.
I WISH I WERE AS FORTUNATE.
YOU HAD A QUARREL-- oh, JAMIE, WORSE?! WHAT POSSESSED YOU BOTH?! I DON'T UNDERSTAND. BRIAN WOULD LAY DOWN HIS LIFE FOR YOU, WITHOUT HESITATION!

AS WOULD I, FOR HIM.
YOU THINK *I* UNDERSTAND? MY LEARNING, MY TRAVELS--SUDDENLY, ***NOTHING*** IS OF ANY USE ANYMORE. NOTHING'S THE SAME, NOTHING MAKES SENSE.
I'VE EVER PRIDED MYSELF ON MY RATIONALITY-- I SAW THINGS, COMPREHENDED THE WORLD, AS IT ***WAS!***

ONLY NOW-- TOO LATE-- I BEGIN TO SUSPECT THAT I'VE BEEN ***BLIND*** ALL THESE YEARS.
THE TRUMPETS ARE *SOUNDING.* I MUST GO.

WISH HAD WORDS...
NO NEED.
PLEASE-- TAKE THIS KERCHIEF, JAMIE. WEAR MY ***FAVOR*** IN THE LISTS.

NEXT TO MY HEART.

HEN WAS THE LAST TIME I HELD LANCE? PALESTINE--EARLIER?! ERTAINLY NOT SINCE LONG EFORE I STARTED HOME.
TRUST I ON'T MAKE O GREAT FOOL OF YSELF-- FOR LI'S SAKE.

I WONDER WHAT PROMPTED THAT BOY TO CHALLENGE ME. WHEN FIRST WE MET, HE WASN'T AT ALL EAGER TO CROSS SWORDS IN A FAIR FIGHT. HE MADE THE USUAL THREATS AS HE LEFT...
...BUT I WAS SURE THEY WERE JUST FOR SHOW.
WHATEVER I AM, IT'S CERTAINLY NOT INFALLIBLE. HOW COMFORTING.

I ACTED LIKE A FOOL WITH BRIAN. AS SOON AS THIS BUSINESS IS DONE...
... I'LL SEEK HIM OUT AND MAKE AMENDS.
READY TO LEARN SOME PROPER MANNERS, SCOTSMAN?

SIR JAMES--?!
HE'S RIDING LIKE A BLOODY NOVICE!
GET YOUR MIND ON YOUR WORK, MY LAD, OR COME THE NEXT CHARGE YOU'LL BE EATING DIRT!
NOT IF I'VE ANYTHING TO SAY ABOUT IT, BROTHER.

MY OBSIDIAN PENDANT IS HEWN FROM THE SAME STONE...

"... AS THINE INFERNAL SERVANT. AS YOU COMMAND IT...

"SO MAY I."

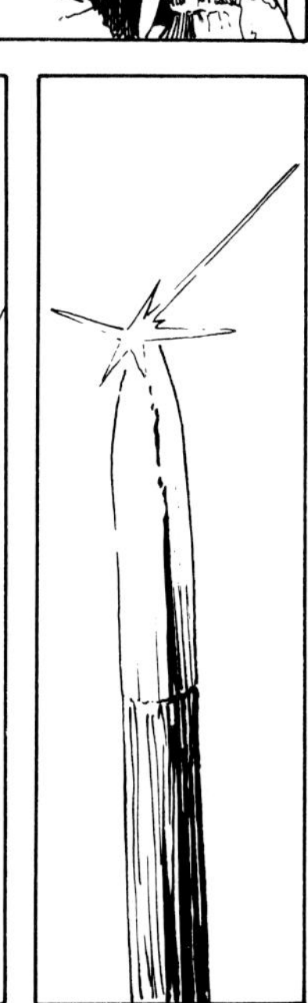

I'VE TAKEN YOUR MEASURE, DUNREITH!

THIS TIME, YOU'LL FALL!

FATHER! SIR BURGO'S LANCE-- ITS POINT ISN'T BLUNTED, IT'S TIPPED WITH STEEL!
AHAHRRR!
FOUL, MY LORD!
SIR BURGO'S MOST GROSSLY VIOLATED THE RULES OF THIS TOURNEY-- AND CHIVALRY ITSELF-- HE'S ATTEMPTED MURDER! SHALL WE ARREST--?!!
NOT YET, CHENIER. LEAVE THIS IN DUNREITH'S HANDS UNLESS HE SEEKS OUR AID--OR IS UNABLE TO CONTINUE.
FATHER, YOU CAN'T-- HE'S WOUNDED!
AND THEREFORE, CHILD, ALL THE MORE DEADLY.
THAT WAS NO ACCIDENT-- HE'S COMING FOR ME AGAIN!

TEN THOUSAND DEVILS IN HELL-- BAD AS THE WOUND WAS, THIS JUST MADE IT WORSE!
I CAN'T RIDE AND FIGHT-- THAT'S SUICIDE!
MY BEST HOPE IS TO FINISH THIS MESS...
...ON THE GROUND.
A LAST CHANCE, BURGO-- YIELD--
--LAY DOWN YOUR SWORD!
I SHALL DO SO GLADLY--

ONCE I'VE BURIED T IN YOUR POXY HEART!
SO BE IT.
WHY THIS ATTACK? IT MAKES NO SENSE--

-- UNLESS... BURGO'S LORD IS A FRIEND OF EDMUND'S.
AND EDMUND IS SUSPECTED OF HIGH TREASON!

THERE'S THE DRAGON I REMEMBER!
TO THE UNTUTORED EYE, ANNE, YOUR CAT'S PAW HAS ALL THE ADVANTAGES: YOUTH, STRENGTH, AND-- I ASSUME THANKS TO YOU-- AN INHUMAN BERSERKER FURY. MOREOVER, HE FIGHTS A BADLY WOUNDED FOE. THE OUTCOME WOULD SEEM TO BE INEVITABLE.
AND INDEED, IT IS.
IS EDMUND PLOTTING REBELLION?
DOES HE KNOW I'VE BEEN SENT TO STOP HIM, IF HE IS?!
IS BURGO HIS PAWN--
-- A MEANS TO ELIMINATE ME WITHOUT AROUSING UNDUE SUSPICION?!
HAS TIME SO CHANGED THE MAN--
-- HAS HATE, OR AMBITION, SO TWISTED HIS SOUL-- THAT HE WOULD BETRAY OUR FRIENDSHIP? I CANNOT BELIEVE THAT.
BUT EVERY OTHER BELIEF OF MINE SEEMS SUDDENLY BUILT OF STRAW, ON SAND--

--WHY NOT THIS AS WELL?!
GOD REST YOUR SOUL, BOY.
I DIDN'T WANT YOUR LIFE, BUT YOU LEFT ME NO ALTERNATIVE.
JAMIE!
ELLIANNE, STAY AWAY-- THIS IS...
I'VE SEEN DEAD MEN BEFORE-- IT'S *YOU* I CARE ABOUT!
HOW FIERCE YOU ARE! I'LL SURVIVE--THOUGH I'LL BE DOING NO RIDING FOR A FAIR WHILE.
I WON'T BE ABLE TO MEET WITH BRIAN ANY TIME SOON-- *DAMN!*

ORGIVE ME, ELLI, YOUR AVOR...
LET ME HAVE THAT, SIR KNIGHT-- PERHAPS I CAN RESTORE IT.
IF SO, MILADY, I AM IN YOUR DEBT-- FOR IT IS... PRECIOUS TO ME.

NO LESS THAN TO ME.
I WARNED YOU.
AND THE LESSON HAS AT LAST BEEN LEARNED. ASK WHAT YOU WILL, BROTHER...
...I SHALL OBEY.

THAT NIGHT--WITH THE NEW MOON INVISIBLE AGAINST A DARKLING SKY...
JAMIE--?
WERE YOU WAITING FOR ME, ELLIANNE-- *WELL!*
BLESS MY SOUL, YOU *HAVE* CHANGED!
DON'T LAUGH, PLEASE. IT'S ONE OF LADY ANNE'S GOWNS; SHE INSISTED I WEAR IT--IN YOUR HONOR.
IT'S ONE I DON'T DESERVE.
OH! YOU THINK IT'S TOO BRAZEN!
I... I'M NOT THE PERSON TO ASK, WHERE YOU'RE CONCERNED.
I COULD NEVER THINK POORLY OF YOU, NO MATTER THE PROVOCATION.
FROM THE FIRST MOMENT--WHEN YOU FACED ME, KNIFE IN HAND, AFRAID YET REFUSING TO BE COWED--I THOUGHT YOU WERE THE MOST WONDROUS CREATURE I'D EVER ENCOUNTERED.
HAVE I SPOKEN OUT OF TURN?

GRACIOUS, *NO!*
FORGIVE MY IMPERTINENCE--
--BUT IT HURTS ME TO SEE YOU STILL SO TROUBLED. IS THERE NOTHING I CAN DO TO EASE YOUR PAIN?!
I DON'T-- I NEVER-- HOW OLD DO YOU THINK I AM?

WHAT HAS THAT TO--?!
THIRTY--NO MORE THAN MIDDLE AGE, CERTAINLY.
I'M SIX YEARS OLDER THAN YOUR FATHER.
I NEVER REALIZED IT BEFORE RETURNING TO ENGLAND AND MEETING THOSE I'D KNOWN IN MY YOUTH. THEY'VE ALL AGED--THEIR LIFETIME PASSED--YET I HAVE NOT. WHY IS THAT?!

I'VE NEVER HAD ANY FAITH IN THE UNSEEN, THE SO-CALLED MYSTERIES OF THE GODDESS-- IN MAGIC-- YET NOW I SENSE IT, I ENCOUNTER IT, WHEREVER I GO!
WITHIN THE ANCIENT, SACRED CIRCLE, I FOUGHT DEMONS!
TWICE, I'VE SPOKEN WITH A DRAGON-- BOTH TIMES IT SAVED MY LIFE--BRIAN GRIFFON, DAMN THE ROGUE, SAYS WE ARE ONE! HOW CAN MAN BE DRAGON, HOW CAN SUCH A BEAST EVEN EXIST?!
AND YET, TODAY, I BEHELD A FAIRY CREATURE-- SHAPED LIKE A WOMAN, WITH GOSSAMER WINGS, BUT AS SMALL AS A MAN'S HAND. SHE HAD BEEN RAPED-- DEFORMED INTO SOMETHING FOUL AND HIDEOUS-- BY EVIL!
IMPOSSIBLE, I TELL MYSELF. BUT IF SO, WHAT DID I SEE?! EITHER IT'S TRUE-- AND REAL-- OR I AM LOST IN MADNESS. AND THE HELL OF IT IS, I DON'T KNOW WHICH FATE IS WORSE!
WHO'S OUT THERE, ELLIANNE, WHAT DO THEY WANT FROM ME?!
WHO AM I?!!
MY POOR DEAR...
... MY POOR, POOR LOVE.
I... FORGIVE ME, I... SHOULD NOT HAVE...
YOU SAID LOVE.
MY HEART SPOKE, I FEAR, TOO SOON.
JAMIE, WE MUST GO IN TO DINNER. EVERYONE EXPECTS...
THEY CAN WAIT.
THIS IS MY DUCAL SIGNET.
SINCE MY FATHER'S DEATH, IT HAS NEVER LEFT MY FINGER.
ELLIANNE, IF YOUR HEART SPOKE TRUE...

THEY STARTED WITHOUT US.
MY FATHER'S FRIENDS AND VASSAL LORDS-- I DON'T MUCH LIKE THEM.
THERE'S LITTLE TO LIKE. THESE MEN ARE JACKALS TO EDMUND'S LION, BASKING IN HIS GLORY, PROTECTED BY HIS STRENGTH, FEEDING OFF HIS SCRAPS-- LOYAL ONLY SO LONG AS IT SUITS THEM. THEY'D LOVE NOTHING BETTER THAN TO TEAR HIM DOWN, AND SET THEMSELVES IN HIS PLACE.
IN THE STRANGEST, MOST FARAWAY OF LANDS, I WAS NEVER SO ALONE AS EDMUND De VALERE, SEATED AT HIS OWN TABLE.
JAMIE!
TAKE YOUR SEAT, MOST NOBLE OF KNIGHTS, THAT WE MAY SALUTE YOUR TRIUMPH!

A MAN DIED, MY LORD, IS THAT CAUSE FOR CELEBRATION?
A FOOL RECEIVED FITTING PUNISHMENT FOR HIS CRIME, MY LADY. WOULD YOU RATHER BURGO FITZWARREN WERE HERE AND DUNREITH ROTTING IN THE GROUND?
WHY, YOU WEAR THE DRAGON SIGNET!

DOST MEAN, MY LORD DUKE, WHAT I THINK?
A BOND, EDMUND, NOTHING MORE.
NOR LESS. OLD FRIEND, YOU DO ME HONOR!
DRINK OF MY CUP, JAMES DUNREITH-- IT IS FOR THOSE MOST BELOVED IN THIS HOUSEHOLD BY ITS MISTRESS AND MASTER.

"PERFECT-- SHE IS A VIRGIN AND HE HAS NEVER TRULY LOVED; IN THEIR OWN WAY, EACH IS INNOCENT-- THE IDEAL SACRIFICE."

ONLY A SIP, EDMUND...

HE DRAINED THE CUP DRY!
THIS IS TOO MUCH FOR ME, I'LL ONLY--
--WONDERFUL!

I WANT MORE-- FILL THE CUP AGAIN--
--TO ITS BRIM!

EMPTY, M'LORD-- CAN YOU DO AS WELL?

IS DRINK ALL YOU CAN DO, SIR JAMES?
DANCE WITH ME--
--OR HAS YOUR WOUND LEFT YOU TOO WEAK?

WHEREVER YOU LEAD, WENCH...
...I'LL FOLLOW!
WORDS, SIRRAH!
PROVE THYSELF-- AND THY METTLE-- WITH DEEDS!

SHE CIRCLES THE RING OF TABLES...
...FLAUNTING HERSELF TO THOSE WHO DARE NOT RESPOND...

...BUT MOST OF ALL TO THE ONE WHO CANNOT RESIST.
AROUND THEM, THE ROOM FALLS SILENT-- EVEN THE HEARTHFIRE BURNS WITHOUT A SOUND.

THEY KISS AND CARESS--

--STRIPPING OFF THEIR HUMANITY WITH THEIR CLOTHES...

...UNTIL THEY BECOME LITTLE BETTER THAN ANIMALS, FRANTICALLY HEEDING SOME PRIMAL INSTINCT...
...DRIVEN BY FORCES BEYOND THEIR COMPREHENSION TO CONSUMMATE THIS ANCIENT, TERRIBLE PASSION.
THERE IS NO LOVE IN WHAT THEY DO, AND LITTLE PLEASURE.
IT IS AN ACT OF VIOLENCE, RIFE WITH DELIBERATE PAIN.
AND AS THEY-- AND THE RITUAL-- BUILD TO A CLIMAX, A CRUMBLED RUIN OF A WALL SURROUNDING THE CASTLE BEGINS TO GLOW-- CASTING LAND AND SKY IN HUES OF BLOOD, DEMARKING GLENOWYN AS A PLACE OF ELDRITCH POWER, LONG SINCE VIOLATED AND CONSECRATED TO SHADOW, THE DARK FORCE-- EVIL!
NOW, TWO MORE INNOCENTS STAND POISED ABOVE THE SAME ABYSS.

AND ARE CAST OVER THE EDGE.

WITH THIS SWORD, I -- EDMUND DeVALERE, EARL OF GLENOWYN, RUNESIRE OF THE WESTERN MARCHES -- CLAIM THEIR IMMORTAL SOULS!
ELLIANNE!?!
WITH THEIR POWER, I CLAIM THIS REALM!!

FOR AELFRIC THE BLACKSMITH OF GLENOWYNSHIRE AND ROWENA, DAUGHTER OF SIMEON, THIS IS THE HAPPIEST NIGHT OF THEIR YOUNG LIVES...
...THE NIGHT OF THEIR MARRIAGE.
BY THE HUNTER!
BLESSED GODDESS-- DEMONS!!

GHYURRGH!
OBSIDIAN CLAWS TEAR AS EASILY THROUGH THE FLESH OF ANCIENT OAKS...
...AS THAT OF MEN...
...AND SINCE THIS TREE IS ONE OF THE GUARDIANS OF THIS MOST GENTLE GROVE...
...THE CREATURE'S ATTACK DRIVES FORTH THE WOOD NYMPHS THAT DWELL WITHIN.
THE FOUL MIASMA CAST BY ITS DAMNED SPIRIT TWISTS THEIR SHAPES AND SOULS...
...TO MATCH ITS OWN.

LIKEWISE, THEIR LUST FOR BLOOD, THEIR TASTE FOR HUMAN FLESH...
...ARE JUST AS GREAT.
AELFRIC!
YAHHRRRR!
BACK, THOU SPAWN OF THE ABYSS! I, GWYNETH TREHERNE, COMMAND THEE!
BY THE POWER OF THE BRIGHT LADY...
... THOU SHALT PROFANE THIS HALLOWED GROUND-- AND HARM HER CHILDREN-- NO LONGER!

AAIIEEE!
MY WAND-- NO! THIS CANNOT BE!
THAT WAS A TRUE WAND, CONSECRATED -- LIKE THE PRIESTESS HERSELF-- TO THE SERVICE OF THE GODDESS, IMBUED WI' HER ESSENCE!
SUPPOSEDLY, NO CREATURE OF EVIL CAN EVEN BEAR THE SIGHT OF THE SILVER STAFF, MUCH LESS BREAK IT!
YET THIS ABOMINATION'S DONE BOTH!
THE SKY-- STORM'S RISIN', A BAD ONE, AS EAMONN FORETOLD--
--BY ALL THAT'S HOLY--
--THE BLACK DRAGON!?!
BUT IT'S A CREATION OF THE SPIRIT-- BOUND TO JAMES DUNREITH'S SOUL, FOR ONLY HIM TO SEE-- IT SHOULD NA' BE MANIFESTIN' ITSELF IN THE REAL WORLD!
IT BELLOWS-- IT SCREAMS-- IN AGONY, AS IF IT'S BEIN' CUT TO THE VERY HEART! THA' MUST PORTEND SOME THREAT, SOME DANGER, TO JAMIE-- BUT WHAT?!

YEURRGH*
AND WHERE DO THESE MONSTERS FIT IN--
--ah, HELL!
THEIR DAMNED CRYSTAL HIDES-- I'D DO BETTER HACKING AT SOLID ROCK-- WHOA?!!
TOO CLOSE, THA' WAS!
THEY'RE FASTER'N CATS!
TH' CHRIST--
--I'M DONE!
WAIT--
--HOLY MOTHER, I'M DAFT--
--OR IT'S THE WORLD, ALL GONE MAD!
JAMIE--?!?
WITHIN THE EYES OF A DEMON, THE SOUL OF DUNREITH--
--JAMIEUNGH*

BLESSED LADY...
... MOTHER OF THE UNIVERSE...
... STAND BY THY DAUGHTERS...

Koff!
KOFF gkagh KOFF!
MERCY, THE STENCH!
AM I DEAD, THEN? BE THIS, THE CHRISTIAN HELL ?!
SURE ENOUGH, IT LOOKS THE PART. BUT IT'S ONLY THE GLADE. SUN'S PAST THE TREETOPS -- IT'S MID-MORNING!
WHO'S THIS-- PHILLIP OF ANTRIM, ONE OF LOCKSLEY'S LADS.
MY BOW'S BROKE TO KINDLING, WOLFSHEAD-- I'M GRATEFUL FOR THE GIFT O' YUIRS.
SLEEP WELL, MY FRIEND. YOU'VE EARNED YUIR REST.
FOUGHT LIKE A TIGER, HE DID-- AN' SIR NIGEL B'SIDE HIM-- FOR ALL THE GOOD IT DID 'EM.
OR ANYONE HERE.

PRIESTESS AN' VIRGIN BRIDE--
--BOTH AS BEFOULED AND TAINTED AS THIS GARDEN.
DAMN-- GOD DAMN-- BE THERE NO JUSTICE?! HOW CAN THE POWERS OF LIGHT TOLERATE SUCH AN ABOMINATION?! HOW?!!
MADNESS! MADNESS!!
BROTHER WILLIAM!
YOU'RE THE... STRANGER... BRIAN GRIFFON... oh, SAINTED FATHER, IT WAS ONLY YESTERDAY I BOUND AELFRIC AND ROWENA IN HOLY WEDLOCK...?
THEY WANTED THEIR MARRIAGE BLESSED...
... BY THE OLD WAYS...
... AS WELL AS THE NEW.
I, IN MY WEAKNESS-- I SAW NO HARM IN'T -- TO MY EVERLASTING SHAME, I... CONSENTED! SEE HOW GOD HAS PUNISHED MY WICKEDNESS, MY LACK OF FAITH!
ANY GOD CAPABLE O' THIS...
...ISN'T WORTH BELIEVING IN!
AN ARROW THROUGH HER HEART, THAT'S WHAT'S NEEDED-- TO END THE LADY GWYNETH'S TORMENT AS I DID A FAERY-LASS CURSED THE SAME WAY.
BUT I CANNOT.
BY MY TROTH, I'LL NA' GIVE THOSE PITSPAWN AN' THEIR BASTARD MASTER THE SATISFACTION-- THIS VICTORY-- NA' WI'OUT A FIGHT!
YOU, WILLIAM! YOU KNOW THE ROAD TO MARBURY TOWN?!
YYESSS.
GOOD! YOU'LL HELP ME FIRST, WI' THESE POOR, WEE LASSIES-- AN' THEN, HIE YUIRSEL' NORTH TO FIND ME ROBIN OF LOCKSLEY!
THE OUT-LAW?!!

THE SAME! YOU'RE TO TELL HIM IT'S WAR-- THE LIGHT AN' THE SHADOW-- AN' HE'S TO BRING EVERY SOUL WHO CAN CARRY A WEAPON!
NO ARGUMENT, PRIEST-- I SPEAK FOR DUNREITH, WHO SPEAKS FOR THE QUEEN-- DO AS I SAY!
I...

ROB'S TO COME QUICK AS HE CAN, WE'VE PRECIOUS LITTLE TIME!
BUT IF I'VE GUESSED RIGHT, THEN GODDESS WILLING, IT SHOULD BE ENOUGH!
TEE HEE TEE HEE TEE HEE

GODDESS-- I SURVIVED BECAUSE THE DEMON WAS ONCE MY FRIEND AN' HE CHOSE TO SPARE ME. BUT THE PRIEST--?
DOES HIS GOD THEN CARE FOR HIS OWN BETTER'N YOU DO YUIRS, LADY? P'RHAPS IT'S TRUE THEN-- THE OLD DAYS, THY WAYS...
...ARE DONE.

GLENOWYN CASTLE...
THE GRIFFON SEEKS TO RAISE AN ARMY AGAINST ME--HA!
WOULD IT NOT BE BETTER, BROTHER, IF THAT SUMMONS WERE NEVER DELIVERED?
EVER THE VOICE OF CAUTION, eh, ANNE?

I COUNSEL NO MORE THAN SIMPLE COMMON SENSE-- ELIMINATE THE THREAT, NOW! SLAY THE PRIEST AND MOST ESPECIALLY BRIAN GRIFFON!
NO. NOT YET.
WHY, EDMUND?!
I PREFER HAVING HIM AND ROBIN HOOD AND THEIR NO DOUBT FORMIDABLE HOST-- INDEED, I WANT ALL WHO CAN DO ME HARM-- GATHERED BEFORE MY GATES, LAYING SEIGE TO MY IMPREGNABLE KEEP...

...THE BETTER THEN TO DESTROY THEM!
REJOICE, MY DARLING...
...THE HOUR OF TRIUMPH WILL SOON BE AT HAND!
THE FIRE IS GONE FROM YOU, ANNE.
HOW STRANGE, HOW SAD, IT WAS YOU WHO SET ME ON THIS PATH, WHO INITIATED ME INTO THE ANCIENT MYSTERIES-- TAUGHT ME, PROTECTED ME, WALKED JOYFULLY BY MY SIDE EVERY STEP OF THE WAY. 'TIL NOW.

TO LOSE HEART WHEN WE'RE SO CLOSE--!
LORD EDMUND--!
BARON RUPERT, LADY ALAIS!
I WISH TO THANK YOU BOTH FOR YOUR SUPPORT IN THIS ENDEAVOR. IT WENT HARD WITH YOU, I KNOW, WHEN YOUR FELLOW NORMAN LORDS HEARD OF YOUR ALLIANCE WITH "THAT ARROGANT, CHURLISH, INSUFFERABLE HALF-BREED WELSH BASTARD!"
THOSE, MY LORD EARL, ARE MERELY THE SLIGHTS OF DOGS WHO ENVY YOUR ACCOMPLISH-MENTS. WE PAY THEM NO HEED.

YOU DO ME HONOR, LADY.
DECEITFUL TROLLOP-- YOU DESPISE ME AS MUCH AS ANY, BUT YOU HUNGER MORE FOR POWER. IF IT SERVED YOUR ENDS, YOU'D BETRAY ME IN A TRICE.
YOU LIFTED NOT A FINGER, SPOKE NOT A WORD, WHEN I ENSORCELLED JAMES AND ELLIANNE-- I SAW YOUR FACES, YOU REVELLED IN THEIR PAIN AND CHEERED THEIR FELL DAMNATION!
WE ARE WITNESSES TO YOUR POWER, EDMUND; NOW MORE THAN EVER YOUR FATE, YOUR WILL, ARE OURS.
IN TRUTH? WILT THOU PLEDGE THINE ALL TO ME, TO MY SERVICE, TO MY CAUSE-- WILT SWEAR TO DO WHATE'ER I REQUIRE...
... TO YIELD WHATSOE'ER I DEMAND?
WITH ALL OUR HEARTS, MOST GRACIOUS LIEGE!

THEN, FOOLS...
...DIE FOR ME!
WHUAAAA--?!
AYAEII!

EDMUND!
IS THIS SOME JEST?!
BASTARD 'BREED, WHAT'S HE PLAYING AT?! NEVER SHOULD HAVE LISTENED, NEVER TRUSTED--!
WHERE... ARE WE...?

EDMUND-- FOR GOD'S SAKE-- SPARE US!
WE'RE LOYAL, WE'RE YOUR FRIENDS--
--HAVE MERCY

RRGKH!
NOT MERCY...
...NOR FRIENDS...

...SAVE THE ONE...
...WHO SLAYS.
I STAND ALONE.
GREAT BEAST-- COME FORTH!

"THOU **AVATAR** THAT ART THE ELDRITCH HEART AND SOUL OF THE REALM, OF THIS MOST NOBLE LAND--

"-- HEAR AND HEED THE WORDS OF THE **MASTER OF GLENOWYN**...

"... **RUNESIRE** OF THE WESTERN MARCHES!

BY BLOOD HAVE I CLAIMED THE **POWER** THAT IS MY BIRTHRIGHT, BY WILLING SACRIFICE DO I CLAIM THE PLACE SO LONG DENIED ME, BY ALL THAT I AM AND WAS AND EVER SHALL BE I CLAIM MY **DESTINY**--
--DRAGON!
I SUMMON THEE!!

DAYS LATER...
GLAD TO SEE YOU, ROB-- YOU MADE FAIR TIME.
DID MY BEST, SCOTSMAN.
BY WEEK'S-END, WE'LL BE READY. WE COULD USE MORE TRAINED SOLDIERS, THOUGH. FOR ALL ITS SIZE, OUR ARMY'S LITTLE BETTER THAN A RABBLE.
WE'LL HAVE TO MAKE DO.
FIGHTING EDMUND'S HOUSEHOLD GUARD, PERHAPS.
BUT AGAINST DEMONS--
--BRIAN, NOT A HOPE.
THAT'S WHY WE'RE HERE.
THE MA'M'S ALREADY GONE, ROB, AND HER DAUGHTER'S SOON TO FOLLOW.
POOR WEE THING-- BUT AT LEAST THE BABE'S PURE, UNSULLIED SOUL WILL ENTER HEAVEN IN A STATE OF GRACE.

GODDESS BE PRAISED.
I'D HOPED AS MUCH.
HOLD, MASTER GRIFFON-- WHAT PAGAN VILLAINY IS AFOOT?!!
ROBIN, A TOLERANT MAN I MAY BE, BUT I'M ALSO A PRIEST OF THE GOSPEL-- THERE ARE SOME THINGS I'LL NOT STAND FOR, EVER! THE CHILD ONLY JUST CAME INTO OUR WORLD, LET HER DEPART IT IN PEACE!
THIS MUST BE DONE, FRIAR TUCK.
ON MY LIFE, SIRRAH, YOU'LL NOT HARM THIS INFANT!
ROBIN, IN MERCY'S NAME-- WILL YOU ALLOW MURDER?!
SHEATHE THE BLADE, SCOTSMAN.

FRIAR TUCK...
... ROBIN HOOD...
... I DO NO MURDER HERE.
OF THAT, I PLEDGE MY WORD OF HONOR.
BUT WE FACE A BATTLE WHEREIN EVEN INNOCENTS MUST PLAY THEIR PART.
LITTLE SISTER, I CRAVE OF THEE THE BOON OF THY IMMORTAL SOUL. WILT PAUSE THIS BRIEF TIME LONGER ON THY JOURNEY UP TO HEAVEN, TO AID US AGAINST THE SHADOW?
IT IS A WEAPON SORELY NEEDED YET ONE WHICH WILL NOT--MUST NE'ER--BE TA'EN FROM THEE...
... BUT FREELY GIVEN, IN JOY AND LOVE.
HOW SAY THEE THEN? DOST HEAR OUR PLEA?
WILT THOU SANCTIFY MY BLADE?

WHERE AWAY?
BROCKEN WOOD-- THAT'S IT UP AHEAD!
LOCALS SAY THE FAERY-FOLK LIVE THERE, THICK AS THIEVES.
AYE-- GLENOWYN'S ALWAYS BEEN RICH IN THAT REGARD. ONE OF THE LAST BASTIONS OF THE OLD RACE.
Y'KNOW, SCOTSMAN, UNTIL THIS MORNING, I'D NEVER SEEN A MIRACLE.
I PRAY, WOLFSHEAD, WE PROVE WORTHY OF THE BAIRN'S TRUST. HER SELFLESS COURAGE HUMBLED US ALL.
AS EDMUND'S MADNESS DISGRACES US.

YOU HATE HIM.
AYE
THAT SWORD THE CHILD BLESSED, IT WASN'T CRAFTED BY HUMAN HANDS.
NO. IT'S FAERY-FORGING, CRYSTAL BONDED WITH SILVER, CONSECRATED WITH THE SIGILS AND ARMS OF DUNREITH.

AND THAT'LL SLAY THE DEMONS?
ITS PURPOSE IS TO HOPEFULLY BIND THOSE TWIN HORRORS.
ART MAD?! THAT BABE GAVE FREELY OF HER SOUL, ROB! THE BLADE IS SANCTIFIED-- TO USE IT TO TAKE A LIFE, ANY LIFE, WOULD BE A WORSE DESECRATION THAN ANYTHING EDMUND'S YET DONE.

AND THEN?
I DON'T KNOW. THAT DECISION'S NA' MINE, THANK THE GODDESS.
DUNREITH'S A SORCERER, SURELY HE CAN SEND THEM BACK TO HELL.
ROB, MY FEAR IS THAT ONE DEMON IS DUNREITH, AN' T'OTHER, ELLIANNE DeVALERE.

DAMNATION, YOU LIE!
IF THAT'S SO, EDMUND'S CUT OFF OUR RIGHT ARM! WE'RE AS GOOD AS--
--JESU CHRISTE!

THEY'RE TOO CLOSE! WE'LL NEVER REACH THEM!
RIDE, SCOTSMAN-- FOR THE SHELTER OF THE TREES!
LEAVE THAT TO ME!
YUIR OUTLAWS!
THEIR DIVERSION SHOULD PROVIDE THE TIME WE NEED.
"BUT ARROWS AN' STEEL ARE NO MATCH FOR THOSE MONSTERS--!"
FEAR NOT, MY FRIEND. I'VE NO INTENTION OF THROWING AWAY THEIR LIVES.
YOUR WORK'S DONE, MY BRAVOS--
--NOW SAVE YOURSELVES! FALL BACK!!

S GLADE'S PERFECT,
T WHAT I NEED.
THIS IS ONE OF THE FEW SPOTS IN THE SHIRE NOT YET RAVAGED BY EDMUND'S PETS. IF THE DUNREITH SWORD DOESN'T DRAW THEM IN, THAT SURELY WILL.
YOU'RE CERTAIN THE DEMONS WILL FOLLOW?
WONDERFUL. THEN THEY'RE RIGHT WHERE WE WANT THEM.
SIDES, I WOULDN'T T IT PAST EDMUND USE HIS MAGICKS SOME INFERNAL EATURE TO SPY ON US...
IS THERE ANYTHING HE CAN'T DO?!
IF HE CLAIMS THE DRAGON-- BECOMES THE WIELDER OF ITS POWER--
--NO.
BLESS MY SOUL!
YOU'D BEST HURRY, MASTER GRIFFON. I THINK OUR TIME'S RUN OUT.
HOLD, BIN--
-- A CUP OF NOONDAY SUN...
... SHROUDED BY MOONLIGHT.
THE NET IS CAST.

GODDESS OR GOD--
--STAND BY ME NOW--
--GRANT ME THE SPEED TO SNARE MY PREY...
...AN' STRENGTH ENOUGH TO HOLD 'EM!
DAMN! I MISSED THE WOMAN--
--WILL SHE STAND BY HER MATE?!
NO, SHE'S FLED!
BUT IN FEAR--OR AT ANOTHER'S COMMAND?! I SAY THE LATTER--
--AN' THAT BODES ILL FOR US.
EDMUND DeVALERE-- BY EARTH AND SEA AND SKY-- BY THE FIRE IN MY SOUL-- I WOULD I WERE CUTTING NOW--
--THROUG YOUR PUSTULEN MAGGO RIDDEN HEART!

LL RLET, YE R--?!
AYE, JOHNNY-- A *SCREAM!*
BY THE ETERNAL, I NEVER WANT TO MEET THE THING THAT MADE IT!
BUT, WILL, ROB'S IN THERE--!

FINE, ALAN. AND THERE'S VT TO BE AFRAID OF, WILL...
... ANYMORE.
GRIFFON--?!
I LIVE, WOLFSHEAD. I BREATHE. GIVEN ETERNITY...
... I MAY EVEN LEARN ONCE MORE TO LAUGH.

IST, TIRED N' I AS AS
THAT WAS A *MAN* ONCE, ROB-- MY FRIEND, AS GOOD AN' NOBLE AS THE BREED COMES -- LOOK WHAT DeVALERE'S DONE TO HIM. AN' TO LADY ELLIANNE AS WELL, THE BASTARD'S OWN DAUGHTER!
I'D HOPED THE SWORD MIGHT SEVER THE ENCHANTMENT THAT TRANS-FORMED JAMIE.

BUT EDMUND'S POWER IS FAR GREATER THAN I EXPECTED-- I'LL WAGER THERE ISN'T A MAGE LIVING WHO'S HIS EQUAL -- AS IT WAS, I BARELY MANAGED TO BIND JAMIE'S DEMON-SELF.
WHAT HOPE HAVE WE THEN, GRIFFON, AGAINST SUCH A MAN?!
DOES IT MATTER? WE'RE IN A WAR THAT MUST BE FOUGHT-- AN' *WON*, ROBIN--
-- LEST *ALL* THAT WE BELIEVE, ALL WE HOLD MOST DEAR, BE LOST, NEVER TO BE REGAINED.

YOU SLEEP THE SLEEP OF THE JUST, MY LOVE.
NO DREAMS, NO DOUBTS, NO... GUILT. I ENVY THAT. I YEARN FOR SUCH SERENITY.
WHY AM I SO WEAK? I WAS ONCE THE STRONGER OF US, EDMUND, WHEN DID THAT CHANGE?! WHAT HAPPENED TO MY HATE?!!

I WAS FIRSTBORN OF GLENOWYN -- THIS IS MY HOME, MY LAND, MY PEOPLE.
YET, BECAUSE OF THE ACCURSED NORMANS...

...I AM LESS THAN NOTHING...
...FORBIDDEN BY THEIR CLERGY EVEN TO PRACTICE THE RELIGION OF MY MOTHER.
RANULF De VALERE MADE HER HIS WHORE--PROFESSED TO LOVE HER WHEN SHE BORE HIM A SON, MY HALF-BROTHER, YOU--
-- YET DID NOTHING TO SAVE HER WHEN THE PRIESTS CONDEMNED HER AS A WITCH...

...AND PUT HER TO THE FLAME.
THROUGH YOU, ELLIANNE, GLENOWYN SHALL BE AVENGED, THE INVADER EXPUNGED...

...OUR BLESSED LAND AT LAST FREED!
THAT'S WHAT I WANT, WHAT I'VE WORKED FOR ALL THESE YEARS.
I SHOULD BE EXULTANT.
ARE YOU AWARE, MY DEAR HEART, MY LOVELY CHILD, OF WHAT I'VE DONE TO YOU?

PERHAPS TH IS WHERE M HATRED AND RAGE HAV GONE--TO ELLIANNE
...FOR ME?
PLEASE UNDERSTAND. AND IF YOU CAN...
...FORGIV

ENOWYN TOR!
ONE OF THE GREAT SEATS OF ENCHANTMENT IN THE REALM-- LIKE STONEHENGE, GLASTONBURY... CA'RYNTH. TONIGHT, WHEN THE FULL MOON RISES, WE'LL MEET THE FAERY-FOLK. EAMONN, LORD OF THE SIDHE, HAS SUMMONED THEM FROM EVERY CORNER OF THE ISLES.
TOMORROW'S THE SUMMER SOLSTICE. WHATEVER EDMUND INTENDS, IF IT'S MAGICKAL IN NATURE, THAT'S THE TIME HE'LL STRIKE.
BREATHE THAT AIR, TUCK-- HAVE YOU EVER TASTED ANYTHING SO FRESH AND SWEET?
ON SUCH AN EVENING, IT'S HARD TO BELIEVE WE'RE FACING ARMAGEDDON.
GRATEFUL FOR YOUR HELP, ROB.
WE STAND BY OUR FRIENDS, BRIAN. I WOULDN'T MIND A BLADE, THOUGH. I FEEL NAKED WITHOUT ONE.
STEEL, ROB-- COLD IRON-- IT'S ANATHEMA TO THE OLD RACE...
ATH
THE
ICH.
NO WILLIES, TUCK, ABOUT STANDING IN A PAGAN HOLY SITE?
AFTER MUCH CONTEMPLATION-- AND PRAYER, MASTER GRIFFON-- I'VE DECIDED THAT IF GOD IS INDEED THE ALMIGHTY, THEN WHAT WE ENCOUNTER HERE WILL MERELY BE FURTHER MANIFESTATIONS OF HIS GLORY. SO, YOU SEE, THIS IS THEREBY HIS HOLY SITE AS WELL.
A NEAT ARGUMENT, I LIKE IT. HAVE A DRAM.
SS
M
ITE...
...PARCHED!?!
MOTHER OF THE LAMB--
--ROB, BRIAN, LOOK YOU-- DID YOU SEE?!!

THEY'RE HERE.
THE GREAT CIRCLE'S BEING DRAWN ABOUT US.
MY GOD...
...IT'S SO... BEAUTIFUL!

SISTERBROTHERS-- **FOULNESS!**
PITSPAWN-- **ABOMINATION**-- IT PROFANES THIS GENTLE PLACE, OUR VERY EXISTENCE! ITS TOUCH BE **FELL DAMNATION!**

EAMONN!
Y' LOOK WELL, YUIR HAND'S HEALED!
AS I SAID IT WOULD, YOUNGLING. I WAS LUCKY.
THY MASTER, I SEE, WAS LESS SO.

AMONG THE BARROW-FOLK, I AM **KING**. ALL WHO ARE OF THE WOODLANDS ARE IN MY CHARGE AND UNDER MY PROTECTION. MOREOVER, OF THIS GATHERING, I HAVE BEEN APPOINTED **LORD**.
I BID THEE AND THY COMPANION WELCOME, ROBIN HOOD...
...AS A FATHER MIGHT HIS KIN.

BY THE POWER OF THIS PLACE AND THOSE ASSEMBLED HERE--
--IN THE NAME OF WE TO WHOM THESE ISLES HAVE BEEN HOME SINCE THE DAWN OF LIFE, AND OF **SHE** WHO IS OUR MOST REVERED **MISTRESS**--
--I **CLOSE** THIS SACRED CIRCLE.
BRIAN-- SOMETHING'S HAPPENING-- THE **DEMON?!!**

BRIAN...?
I FEEL SO... STRANGE!
MOST GRACIOUS PRINCE...
...THY PEOPLE DO THEE HOMAGE.

THE LANGUAGE YOU USE-- IT ISN'T ENGLISH, BUT I UNDERSTAND...
...AND SPEAK IT MYSELF! AND YOU SAY THESE PEOPLE ARE "MINE?!" BRIAN, THEY AREN'T HUMAN!
NOR, IN TRUTH, ARE YOU, JAMIE.
MADNESS, OR SOME CRUEL JEST!
NEITHER, MY LORD NOR A DREAM -- TH IS THE JAMES DUNRE THAT MIGHT HAVE BEEN, THAT SHOULD
NO! NO!! I DENY IT! I'M A MAN!!
NOT ANY LONGER, JAMIE, THANKS TO EDMUND De VALÈRE.
REFUSE US-- CAST ASIDE THY HERITAGE-- AN' WE ARE ALL OF US DOOMED, AND DAMNED! THOU HAST DENIED THY TRUE SELF O'ERLONG, MY PRINCE, AN' INNOCENTS HAVE PAID THE PRICE.
GAZE INTO THE VAULT OF THY MEMORY AND TELL ME THEN IF I LIE!
IF ALL THIS BE BUT FANTASY!
M-MY HANDS--?!?
VISIONS-- THAT ALL CAN SEE--
--I AM ENSORCELLED BY A FALSE FRIEND-- oh, ELLIANNE, NOT YOU, TOO-- EDMUND, YOUR OWN FLESH AND...
...BLOOD. THE NIGHTMARE THAT HAUNTED ELLI WHEN WE MET, OF HER WALLOWING IN A CHARNAL SEA OF CORPSES, TEARING THE FLESH FROM THE DEAD AND THOSE WHO YET LIVED, TO GORGE HERSELF 'TIL HER BELLY ACHED.
A PREMONITION-- A FORETELLING OF WHAT WAS TO COME--
--WHAT HAS NOW BEEN.
AND I STOOD BY HER.
I, TOO KILLED
I... FEAST

AND RAVAGED--
-- BOTH BODY AND SOUL--
-- OF A MOST NOBLE, BLESSED GENTLEWOMAN.

GWYNETH...?

YOU!
SEEKEST THOU, DUNREITH, TO HIDE THY TRUE NATURE...
... BEHIND A PRETTY SEEMING?

FOR SHAME, PRINCE!
I'LL NOT LET THEE!

MY FLESH--TORN--BUT I DO NOT BLEED!
BENEATH IT-- NOT BONE, BUT DAEMONIC CRYSTAL!

SEE, BRETHREN-- FOR ALL HE APPEARS TO BE A LORD OF LIGHT...
... AT HEART HE REMAINS A CREATURE OF SHADOW!
IT IS AS THE PROPHECY FORETOLD--
--OUR SAVIOR HAS BECOME INSTEAD THE DESTROYER!

I TERRIFY THEM-- NO LESS THAN I DO MYSELF. BRIAN, WHAT HAVE I BECOME?!
THE FAILURE IS AS MUCH MINE-- FOR WHEN MY LORD HAD NEED OF HIS GRIFFON, I WAS NOT THERE.
HELP ME--!
I TRIED--
-- BUT YOU WOULDN'T LISTEN.
AND NOW-- IT'S TOO LATE?!

ROB, WHAT DO WE WITNESS HERE?
PERHAPS THE LAST NIGHT OF A WORLD. DUNREITH'S OF THE OLD RACE, TUCK, AND NEVER KNEW IT-- LOOK THERE!
MATER CHRISTI!
IN LEGEND, THE BLACK DRAGON'S THE SOUL OF THE REALM.
SUPPOSE THAT'S TRUTH! SUPPOSE DUNREITH'S ITS HUMAN VESSEL--ONLY De VALERE'S CHAINED HIM, STRIPPED HIM OF HIS HUMANITY, MADE HIM A SLAVE?

GRIFFON, CAN WHAT WAS DONE TO OUR PRINCE BE UNDONE? CAN De VALERE'S ENCHANTMENT BE BROKEN?!
NO. THROUGH WHAT HE STOLE FROM JAMIE-- AND WHAT HE'S MADE HIM DO-- THE BASTARD'S SUNK HIS HOOKS DEEP INTO THE DRAGON. HE'S MADE HIMSELF AS MUCH THE AVATAR AS JAMIE, WITH THE SAME ACCESS TO ITS POWER.

JAMES DUNREITH, THOU ART OUR PRINCE, OUR LIEGE, THE BRIGHTEST OF OUR HOPES. OUR RESPECT AND LOVE FOR THEE IS BOUNDLESS...
... YET EVIL HATH TAINTED THEE. THOU HAST DONE GREAT HARM TO US-- AND HUMANFOLK AS WELL.
THIS MUST BE ATONED FOR-- THE SCALES BALANCED-- THE BLOOD THOU HAST SHED MUST BE PAID FOR IN KIND.

ALL MY LIFE, I'VE PRIDED MYSELF ON MY RATIONALITY. I TRUSTED MY PHYSICAL SENSES AND BELIEVED IN THE WORLD AS THEY SAW IT. THAT WAS REALITY.
ONLY IT ISN'T. IT'S SO MUCH MORE-- FOR ALL MY WANDERING AND SEARCHING, I'D HARDLY SCRATCHED ITS SURFACE. FOR ALL MY VAUNTED LEARNING...
... I KNOW NOTHING.

BRIAN, I RETAIN THIS SEMBLANCE OF MYSELF ONLY SO LONG AS I STAY WITHIN THIS CIRCLE, IS THAT SO?
AYE.
ARE THERE ANY HERE WHO CAN MATCH EDMUND'S MAGICKS, SHOULD HE COME FOR ME?
YOU. ONCE.
OR SO WE'D PRAYED.
AND I AM HIS CREATURE.

THERE'S BUT ONE ANSWER, MY FRIEND. EDMUND MUST BE STOPPED-- WHAT HE INTENDS IS SO MONSTROUS, THE ATROCITIES ALREADY COMMITTED IN HIS NAME PALE BY COMPARISON.
IF I AM A KEY TO HIS SUCCESS, THEN YOU MUST DEPRIVE HIM OF IT.

MY SINGLE LIFE WILL BE SMALL PAYMENT FOR THOSE I HAVE SLAUGHTERED, BUT IT IS ALL I HAVE TO OFFER.
BRIAN, CAN YOU... WILL YOU...?
AYE, MILORD.
THE DUNREITH BLADE CAN CUT YUIR CRYSTAL...

...THOUGH IT'LL BREAK MY HEART TO DO SO.
ON PERIL OF THY LIFE, GRIFFON, I CRY THEE--
--HOLD!
MAJESTY OF FAERY, IT IS SHE!

I AM MORGAN Le FEY!
JAMES DUNREITH IS MY SON, HE IS THE BLACK DRAGON, HEIR TO MY THRONE AND ALL THE DOMAINS OF FAERY ON THIS WORLD AND ANY OTHER--
--AND THOU SHALT HARM HIM NOT!!

BLESSED LADY-- THE QUEEN!

ROBIN...?!!
DON'T QUESTION, TUCK-- FOR THE NONCE, WATCH AND WONDER, AND ACCEPT.
MOTHER--?!?
BY ALL THAT'S HOLY--

--IT IS YOU!

I WAS TOLD YOU'D DIED WITH FATHER!
IN A SENSE, MY SWEET, I HAD.

THE WORLD IS CHANGING, AND OUR PLACE IN IT GROWS SMALLER WITH EACH PASSING SEASON--
--THANKS IN LARGE MEASURE TO YOU WHO FOLLOW THE ONE GOD, AND WHO LACK IN YOUR HEARTS THE CHARITY OF WHICH YOU ARE SO FOND OF PREACHING!

MISTRESS, I AM THE EARL OF HUNTINGDON-- WHOM SOME CALL ROBIN HOOD-- I CANNOT VOUCH FOR OTHERS OF THE CLOTH, BUT I'LL GLADLY STAND FOR FRIAR TUCK!
HE'S A GOOD MAN, BY ANY LIGHTS!
MAJESTY YOU MAY BE-- AND WELL ABLE TO STRIKE ME DEAD-- BUT YOU'VE NEITHER CAUSE NOR RIGHT TO SPEAK SO OF HIM!
THY COURAGE DOES THEE CREDIT, WOLFSHEAD-- AS DOES THY LOYALTY TO THY FRIEND.
IN GRIEF AND RAGE I MIS-SPOKE, MASTER TUCK-- PROVING EVEN WE OF FAERY ARE PRONE TO HUMAN FRAILTIES-- AND FOR THAT I BEG YOUR PARDON.
YOU ASK, MY SON, 'WHAT HAPPENED?'
HEARKEN, AND I SHALL TELL THEE.
SINCE THE DAWN OF LIFE, CA'RYNTH AND ITS CLAN DUNREITH HAVE BEEN CONSECRATED TO BOTH FAERY AND HUMANKIND, A BRIDGE BETWEEN THE TWO.
WHEN THE ROMAN, JULIUS CAESAR, CAME TO THIS LAND, WE FAILED TO MAKE OUR PEACE WITH HIM. THROUGH YOU, MY SON, WE HOPED TO DO DIFFERENT WITH THE NORMANS.
THOU WERT TO BE OUR PROTECTOR, OUR SHIELD AT COURT AGAINST THE CONQUEROR'S NEW-MADE BARONS AND THEIR PET PRIESTS. BUT UNLIKE WILLIAM AND HIS SONS, THEY DID NOT HONOR OUR ANCIENT RIGHTS AND TITLES. THEY WANTED OUR WEALTH, OUR LAND, OUR POWER--
--OUR VERY LIVES!
"THE CIVIL WAR BROKE THAT FRAGILE PEACE. FOR NINETEEN YEARS, THE FORCES OF THE USURPER STEPHEN FOUGHT THOSE OF THE EMPRESS MATILDA. THOUGH HE WAS AN OATH-BREAKER THRICE OVER, STEPHEN WAS THE ANOINTED KING; BY LAW, WE OWED OUR FEALTY TO HIM.
"BUT OUR HEARTS, OUR TRUE LOYALTY, REMAINED WITH THE RIGHTFUL HEIR-- THE EMPRESS AND HER SON, HENRY.

"TO WED THY SIRE AND BEAR THEE, JAMES, I HAD TAKEN ON A **HUMAN** SEEMING. CONAL DUNREITH WAS A TRUE PRINCE, IN THE BEST SENSE OF THE WORD. HE WOO'D AND WON MY HEART; IN HIS ARMS--TO MY GREAT SURPRISE--FOR THE FIRST TIME IN MY MEMORY, I WAS **HAPPY**.
"I LOVED HIM AS I HAVE NO OTHER. I WOULD HAVE STAYED WITH HIM FOREVER--RENOUNCED NAME, POWERS, HERITAGE.
"BUT IN MY JOY, I FORGOT MY HUMANITY WAS ONLY A SEEMING, AN **ILLUSION**.

"AMBITIOUS MEN RECOGNIZED MY ANCIENT BLOOD--THOUGH NONE REALIZED WHO I **TRULY** WAS. ADJUDGING US **TRAITORS** TO THEIR FALSE KING, THEY CAME TO US IN FRIENDSHIP...
"...TO SLAY MY BELOVED LORD...

"...AND BIND ME WITH COLD IRON--FO
SUCH IS ANATHEMA TO OUR KIND. ITS TOUCH IS AGONY, OFTEN UNTO DEATH. THEY THOUGHT ME HELPLESS.

"THEY LOOKED FORWARD TO HAVING THEIR CRUEL SPORT WITH THE DUKE OF CA'RYNTH'S FAERY WIFE.

"BUT I WON FREE OF THEIR CHAINS...
"...AND TOOK MY JUST--AND LAWFUL--VENGEANCE.
"YET THE COST OF THAT VICTORY PROVED AS TERRIBLE

THE POWER NECESSARY TO BREAK MY CHAINS RAVAGED MY STRENGTH AND HURLED ME BACK NTO MY OWN REALM, AS NEAR TO DEATH AS AN IMMORTAL CAN COME.
"WHEN I RETURNED ONCE MORE TO MY RIGHTFUL SENSES, I DISCOVERED TO MY HORROR THAT THOU WERT A GROWN MAN. WORSE, I FOUND I COULD MANIFEST A PHYSICAL PRESENCE ON EARTH ONLY IN THOSE PLACES STILL CONSECRATED TO ME-- WHICH HAD BECOME PITIFULLY FEW AND FAR BETWEEN.
THOU HADST BEEN RAISED KNOWING NOTHING OF THY TRUE HERITAGE-- HOUGH IT WAS EMBODIED IN THY STRENGTH AND HEALTH, AND THINE NSATIABLE CURIOSITY. I EVER PRAYED THY WANDERINGS WOULD EVENTUALLY RING THEE TO A PLACE WHERE I COULD ONCE MORE GREET THEE...

. BUT NEVER DREAMED HAT, ALONG THY ROAD, HOU WOULDST TAKE IS FRIEND AND OON COMPANION...
. THE SON OF HE NORMAN, De VALERE, WHO SLEW THY FATHER.
I'VE DONE FAR WORSE THAN THAT.
I LOVE HIS DAUGHTER.

FORGIVE ME, MAJESTY.
SPEAK WHAT IS IN THINE HEART, MY LORD OF THE SIDHE...
...I'LL NOT CONDEMN THEE FOR'T.
FOR MYSELF, I WOULD RATHER DIE!

BUT I DARE NOT-- CANNOT-- HOLD MY TONGUE! TOO MUCH IS AT STAKE!
I KNOW THY SON IS THE BLACK DRAGON-- HEIR AND LAST HOPE OF FAERY. BUT DeVALERE HATH DASHED THAT HOPE, DIMMED THE PRINCE'S BRIGHT PROMISE, FOREVER.
JAMES DUNREITH-- THOU HAST BEEN TAINTED BY AN ENCHANTMENT THAT CANNOT BE BROKEN BY ANY POWER OF THE EARTH! THOU HAST COMMITTED CRIMES THAT CAN NEITHER BE FORGIVEN NOR FORGOTTEN. BLOOD PRICE IS DEMANDED-- AND MUST BE PAID!
FAR BETTER THE LINGERING DEATH OF EXTINCTION BROUGHT ABOUT BY THE CHANGING WORLD THAN THE ETERNAL ENSLAVEMENT AND FELL DAMNATION-- WHILE WE YET LIVE-- WHICH WILL BE THE LEGACY OF THE BASTARD EDMUND'S SPELL!

JAMES UNDERSTOOD THAT AND WAS WILLING TO SACRIFICE HIMSELF-- BEFORE THINE INTERVENTION.
I BEG THEE, MORGAN, LET US CONTINUE.
MOTHER...
...EAMONN'S RIGHT.

I HATE TO INTERRUPT, MY LORDS AND LADIES...

LONDON TO GLENOWYN IN TWO NIGHTS AND A DAY. IF I HADN'T RIDDEN THE DISTANCE BESIDE YOU, MAJESTY, I'D NEVER HAVE BELIEVED IT!
OLD I MAY BE, WILLIAM MARSHALL, BUT NOT YET INFIRM--
-- MUCH AS MY SONS MIGHT WISH IT DIFFERENT.
MAKE CAMP HERE. REST BOTH MEN AND HORSES BUT BE READY TO MOUNT ON A MOMENT'S NOTICE BE READY TO FIGHT AS WELL. GLENOWYN IS ENEMY TERRITORY

FROM HERE, I SHALL PROCEED ALONE AND AFOOT. KEEP WATCH 'TIL I RETURN.
AS YOU COMMAND, MY QUEEN.

FOR NO REASON WILL YOU FOLLOW! LIKEWISE-- ON YOUR LIVES AND SOULS-- WILL YOU ALLOW ANY OTHER TO FOLLOW ME. LASTLY, YOU WILL DO NO HARM-- NOR ATTEMPT TO HINDER-- ANY WHO DEIGN TO LEAVE THE TOR. AM I UNDERSTOOD, CAPTAIN?
I'D FEEL BETTER, ELEANOR, GOING WITH YOU ALL THE WAY.

I KNOW. IF I ASKED--AND I MAY YET THIS NIGHT--YOU WOULD ENTER HELL TO DUEL THE DEVIL.
DEAR WILLIAM, YOU MAY BE THE MOST NOBLE KNIGHT IN CHRISTENDOM --IF NOT THE WORLD-- AND OF A SURETY THE FINEST SOLDIER...
...BUT YOU ARE NOT A KING.

AND THIS IS A PATH ONLY ROYAL FEET MAY TRED.

ENGLAND'S QUEEN, I BID THEE WELCOME.
ELEANOR?!?
THE QUEEN--?!
FAERY'S QUEEN, I THANK THEE FOR THY GRACIOUS INVITATION.

NAY!
NORMAN, SHE BE-- ONE OF THE INVADERS WHO HAVE DESPOILED OUR LAND AND BUTCHERED OUR BRETHREN!
DRIVE HER FROM THIS HOLY PLACE-- LEST BY HER PRESENCE, SHE BEFOUL IT UTTERLY!

ANY WHO WISH QUEEN ELEANOR HARM WILL HAVE TO DEAL FIRST WITH ME!
AND ME, MISCREANTS!
AN' ME!
AND ME!

HEAR ME, YOU LORDS AND LADIES OF FAERY-- I AM QUEEN MAGISTER OF THE REALM, MY LIFE BOUND TO THIS LAND BY A SACRED OATH I SWORE-- WITH MY HUSBAND, HENRY PLANTAGENET UPON OUR CORONATION, AND SANCTIFIED WITH THIS CROWN!
I AM QUEEN MAGISTER OF FAERY-- AND THE CROWN SHE WEARS WAS SANCTIFIED BY ME!
VIOLENCE SAID OR DONE ELEANOR OF AQUITAINE IS VIOLENCE DONE ME!

HOW SAY'ST YOU, GENTLES?! IS THAT YOUR WISH?!!
THOU'RT OUR LIEGE, MORGAN. THY WILL...
...BE OUR LAW.

YOU'VE CHANGED, MILORD DUNREITH, SINCE LAST WE MET.
LADY, YOU KNEW ME BETTER THAN I DID MYSELF.
OF COURSE HENRY DID TOO-- THAT' WHY HE AGREED TO YOUR BANISHMEN

BETTER THE KING LOSE YOUR SERVICES THAN THE LAND YOUR LIFE.
NOW, LADY, YOU'RE LIKELY TO LOSE BOTH. ELEANOR, I HAVE COMMITTED SUCH ATROCITIES-- AN ETERNITY OF GOOD WORKS CANNOT BEGIN TO MAKE AMENDS.
THE DRAGON IS THE SOUL OF THE LAND, MY SON, THE SPIRITUAL BOND BETWEEN THE WORLD AND ITS CHILDREN, BOTH HUMAN AND FAERY.
IT REQUIRES A LIVING FOCUS, A VESSEL THROUGH WHICH ITS POWER MAY BE MANIFEST. THAT WAS TO BE THEE...
...ONLY NOW, EDMUND DeVALERE HATH USURPED THY PLACE.
HE PLANS FAR WORSE THAN THAT.
ON MIDSUMMER NIGHT, HE MEANS TO UNLEASH THE DRAGON-- TO SLAY EVERY MAN, WOMAN AND CHILD IN THESE ISLES WHOSE VEINS BEAR EVEN A DROP OF NORMAN BLOOD.
BLESSED MOTHER!
HE CANNOT!
MADNESS!
MORE POWER TO 'IM!
NO LESS'N THE SCUM DESERVE!
HINK YOU ALL, WHAT HIS MEANS-- O HAVE THE POWER OF HE DRAGON SED FOR SUCH A THING!
WHAT MY SON HATH DONE IS BUT THE FUTURE IN SMALL, THE MEREST HARBINGER OF OUR FATE SHOULD EDMUND SUCCEED. THE LAND WILL BE SOAKED DEEP WITH INNOCENT BLOOD THAT CAN NEVER BE WASHED CLEAN. WE WILL BE SCARRED-- INFECTED WITH A CANCER-- THAT NOTHING CAN EXCISE.
OUR CHILDREN WILL BEAR OUR SEEMING, BUT THAT IS ALL. THEY WILL BE NEITHER HUMAN NOR FAERY...
BUT FOUL, WISTED REATURES FOREVER CONSECRATED TO THE SHADOW.
MAJESTY, WHAT THEN ARE WE TO DO?!
IF JAMIE DEPARTS THIS CIRCLE, HE'LL REVERT TO HIS DEMONFORM-- AND BECOME ONCE MORE EDMUND'S SLAVE. IF HE STAYS, THE BASTARD'S SURE TO SEND LADY ELLIANNE TO FREE HIM...

...THEREBY DESECRATING THIS HOLY PLACE, BREAKING ITS POWER AS HE HAS SO MANY OTHERS.
HE CAN, BRI, BUT IT WON'T BE NECESSARY. THE DRAGON'S FOCUS MUST NEEDS BE PARTLY HUMAN, AND SO LONG AS I REMAIN HERE, I AM WHOLLY OF FAERY.
AT LAST, TOO LATE, I UNDERSTAND.

THE DEMON IS THE SHAPE AND SUBSTANCE OF MY HUMANITY.
WHATEVER WE DO--EVEN IF YOU SLAY ME--EDMUND WINS, THE POWER WILL BECOME HIS.
AND IF HE DIES, THE DRAGON CEASES TO BE; ITS POWER WILL BE LOST.

A MASTERFUL PLAN, VERY NEARLY CHECKMATE.
IT TRADES UPON ALL OUR DESIRES FOR LIFE, WHATEVER THE COST. I WONDER, THOUGH, WHICH IS WORSE. A LAND WITHOUT A SOUL...
...OR ONE WHOSE SOUL IS DAMNED.
YOU'RE GOING BACK?

I MUST.
THA'S DAFT, DUNREITH!
OUR CAUSE MAY SEEM HOPELESS, BUT YOU'LL BE GIVING DeVALERE HIS VICTORY ON A PLATTER! OR IS IT THA' YOU LIKE THE THINGS HE OFFERS, AN' HAD YOU DO?!

THIS IS NOTHING TO DO WITH ME, BRI-- IT'S ELLIANNE.
SHE'S AN INNOCENT, AS MUCH A VICTIM AS THOSE POOR SOULS SHE SLAUGHTERED. SHE'S DONE NOTHING TO DESERVE SUCH A FATE.
BRIAN, I *LOVE* HER. I WON'T ABANDON HER.
IF THERE'S A WAY TO SAVE ELLI, I HAVE TO TRY TO FIND IT.

YOUR CONCERN FOR OUR FOSTER DAUGHTER DOES YOU CREDIT, MY NOBLE LORD, BUT DO YOU TRULY BELIEVE HER ANY LESS HONORABLE A SOUL THAN YOU?
OR THAT SHE WOULD FEEL ANY LESS GRIEF AND SHAME, LESS OF A NEED TO BALANCE THE SCALES? WHAT IS DONE-- WHATE'ER ITS GENESIS--
--CANNOT BE UNDONE.
THEN, ELEANOR, AT THE VERY LEAST...

...I OWE HER A CLEAN DEATH.
ARE THERE ANY IN THIS ASSEMBLAGE TO GAINSAY ME?!

BRIAN, YOU AND ROB LAY SIEGE TO GLENOWYN CASTLE. IT MAY DO NO GOOD...
...BUT WHAT'VE WE GOT T' LOSE, eh?!
I'LL MISS YOU, JAMIE.
WE'RE NEITHER OF US DEAD YET.
FAREWELL, BRETHREN. I WISH I'D KNOWN YOU BETTER.
BUT GLAD I AM, EVEN FOR SO BRIEF A TIME AS THIS IN YOUR COMPANY.
MOTHER-- I FIND MYSELF... AFRAID.
THERE'S SO MUCH I WANT TO SAY.
NO LESS THAN I.
BE TRUE TO THY HEART, MY GALLANT BOY-- WHAT THOU ATTEMPT'ST IS MEET AND RIGHT-- IT WILL ARMOR THY SOUL AGAINST EDMUND'S SORCERY.
I PRAY THERE IS A HEAVEN, AND THAT MY HENRY IS WATCHING FROM ON HIGH.
THIS NIGHT, JAMES, YOU DO THE KING--MY HUSBAND AND YOUR FRIEND-- PROUD.
AND THY FATHER AS WELL.
BLESSED St. GEORGE--!?!
GRAAAA
M'LORD EARL-- A DEMON!
TO ARMS, COMRADES!!
SHEATHE YOUR BLADE, MONTJOY!
REMEMBER THE QUEEN'S COMMAND! STAND ASIDE, LET IT PASS!

I... MIND-- IS STILL MINE OWN-- I CAN THINK!
AND... AFTER A FASHION... SPEAK!
TO GLENOWYN, MY LORD EARL, AND FOR THE SAKE OF THE REALM-- HURRY!!

BY THE CHRIST, I THOUGHT I'D SEEN EVERYTHING--!
ELEANOR?!! YOUR MAJESTY, I -- THANK GOD--!
WE RIDE, WILLIAM!
WHERE AWAY?
TO WAR, AND MAYHAP...
...ARMAGEDDON!

HE'S SNAPPED MY LEASH.
WELL, I KNEW THAT MIGHT HAPPEN. IT MAKES NO DIFFERENCE. I'VE GONE TOO FAR, I WON'T BE STOPPED.
BUT I WONDER-- AM I DOING THE RIGHT THING? DO THE ENDS JUSTIFY SUCH FOUL MEANS?!

I LOVE HIM, YET I WILLINGLY-- EAGERLY-- MADE HIM MY CREATURE. A NECESSARY SACRIFICE, I TOLD MYSELF, THE PRICE THAT HAD TO BE PAID.
HE TRUSTED ME, AND I BETRAYED HIM. HE WOULD NEVER HAVE DONE THE SAME TO ME.
DAMN ANNE--HER WEAKNESS, HER WOMANISH DOUBTS, HAVE INFECTED ME! SHE SHOULD UNDERSTAND BEST OF ALL-- OUR LAND, OUR PEOPLE, ARE ENSLAVED! I HAVE A SACRED DUTY TO FREE THEM, BY ANY MEANS, AT ANY COST!
EDMUND--?!
BROTHER ARE YOU WELL?

I COULD NOT SLEEP.
OLDER SHE IS, THAN THAT ROYAL BITCH, ELEANOR, YET SHE APPEARS AS FAIR AND YOUTHFUL AS HER CHILD, ELLIANNE. BECAUSE-- AS WITH JAMIE DUNREITH-- THE FAERY BLOOD RUNS DEEP AND STRONG WITHIN HER.
NOT SO, WITH ME. I AM MORE HUMAN-- TAINTED WITH AGE, CORRUPTED BY MORTALITY.
I NEVER KNEW MY TRUE HERITAGE, ANNE--

-- UNTIL YOU TOLD ME.
HAD YOU NOT, I'D HAVE LIVED A NORMAL LIFE. BEEN PROUD OF WHAT I'D ACHIEVED-- THE PLACE OF HONOR I'D FORGED FOR MYSELF WITH SWEAT AND BLOOD. BUT THOSE FEW WORDS TURNED EVERYTHING TO ASHES.
EDMUND--?
JAMIE IS COMING-- A DEMON STILL, BUT NO LONGER A SLAVE. I MUST PREPARE AN APPROPRIATE RECEPTION...
...FOR MY FRIEND.
FOR MY LOVE.

BY THE LIVING CHRIST, MY HEART STILL ACHES WHENEVER I THINK OF HIM -- YET AT THE SAME TIME, I GLORY IN HIS DEGREDATION!
Oh, ANNE, SEE WHAT YOU'VE DONE?!
THE KNOWLEDGE YOU GAVE HAS MADE ME GREAT.
IT HAS DESTROYED ME!
JAMIE WAS THE MOST BEAUTIFUL FACE-- AND SOUL-- I HAD EVER SEEN. I'D HAVE CHEERFULLY DIED FOR HIM--PAID ANY PRICE TO BE LIKE HIM.

YOU SHOWED ME THAT COULD NEVER BE.
HOW QUICKLY, THEN, I CAME...
...TO HATE HIM.
ELLIANNE--

-- I GRANT THEE A PORTION OF THY FORMER HUMANITY.
THE POWER OF SPEECH, SOME FEW PIECES OF MEMORY.
THERE IS... PAIN!
YES! THERE WAS A MAN WHO CLAIMED TO LOVE YOU! IT WAS HE WHO VIOLATED YOUR VIRGIN BODY-- AND TWISTED IT INTO THIS MISSHAPEN CREATURE YOU HAVE BECOME, AND WILL FOREVER REMAIN!

WHAT ARE YOU DOING?!
IT'S QUITE SIMPLE. BELIEVING WHAT I TELL HER-- BECAUSE IT CONTAINS A GRAIN OF TRUTH-- ELLIANNE'S OWN LOVE FOR JAMIE WILL BECOME PUREST, FIERY HATE, HER ONLY DESIRE TO WREAK FINAL VENGEANCE ON THE FIEND WHO HURT HER SO.
EACH TIME I SEE HIM-- AND YOU, ANNE-- I HEAR THE FATES LAUGHING, MOCKING THE ARROGANT HALF-BREED, NEITHER WELSH NOR NORMAN, HUMAN NOR FAERY...
...WHO HAS NO TRUE PLACE TO CALL HIS OWN...
...AND NONE TO WELCOME HIM...

...OR MOURN HIS PASSING.
BUT I, THE BASTARD-- I ALONE-- POSSESS THE POWER OF THE DRAGON!
AND I'LL WIELD IT IN SUCH A WAY...
...THAT WILL SHATTER THE FOUNDATIONS OF HELL AND HEAVEN!!

WHAT THE DEVIL IS THAT?!!
DEVIL IS RIGHT, FROM THE SOUND OF IT.
I'VE NEVER HEARD SUCH A ROAR. I PRAY I NEVER MEET THE BEAST THAT MA--

GOOD SHOT, ROB!
DID THE JOB, WILL SCARLET.
INTO THE MOAT, LADS-- AND NOT A SOUND FROM ANY OF YOU!

THE FORCES OF MEN HAVE BEGUN THE BATTLE.
IT IS TIME FOR THOSE OF FAERY TO DO THEIR PART.
WILLIAM MARSHALL, WHEN ROBIN HOOD SECURES THE GATE AND LOWERS THE DRAWBRIDGE...
...WE CHARGE, MAJESTY, MY MEN AND I.
THE WOLFSHEAD CUT HIMSELF NO EASY TASK.
I WISH HIM LUCK.

"HENRY PLANTAGENET, REST HIS SOUL, NEVER BELIEVED IN LUCK.
"ONLY IN WINNING."

MILORD, HE'S NEARLY THERE!
DRAW SWORDS, MEN--BE READY!
AND UNTIL YOU HEAR DIFFERENT FROM ME OR THE WOLFSHEAD...
...THE COMMAND IS NO QUARTER.
SO FAR, SO GOOD.

DAMN! HE KICKED THE BRAZIER!

ROB--?!
HELL'S TEETH!
MAKE FOR THE GATE, LITTLE JOHN--QUICK AS YOU CAN!

WHA--?! A FIRE!?!
BY HECATE--ARMED MEN!!
SOUND THE ALARM--FALL OUT THE GUARD--
--WE ARE INVADED!

THEY'VE GOT CROSSBOWS!
THEN DON'T GIVE 'EM A TARGET, DOLT!
RAISE THE PORTCULLIS, JOHN!
SOME OF YOU OTHERS TAKE CARE OF THE BRIDGE--

--THE REST STAND WITH ME!

THE BRIDGE IS DOWN, THE GATE'S OPEN!
FOR GOD, St. GEORGE, THE QUEEN AND ENGLAND--
--CHARGE!

SLAY EVERY MOTHER'S-SON WHO FOLLOWS DeVALERE. AND AS FOR THE RENEGADE EARL HIMSELF--
--HE ABOVE ALL IS NOT TO SEE TOMORROW'S SUNRISE!

THOSE BE ROYAL TROOPS!
AYE, BOY-- AN' RIDIN' WI' OUT-LAWS!
IT MATTERS NOT WHO THEY BE. THEY ATTACK OUR LORD--
--THEY PAY THE PRICE!!

REPORT, THOMAS.
MAIN WALL'S BEEN BREACHED, M'LUD, AS YOU CAN SEE. THAT FIRE'S A BAD 'UN, TOO-- I'VE NO MEN TO SPARE TO KEEP IT FROM SPREADING.
CAREFUL, SIR-- YOU'RE AN AWFULLY TEMPTING TARGET FOR LOCKSLEY'S ARCHERS, DAMN THEIR EYES.
OUR LOSSES?

TOO MANY, TOO FAST.
CAN YOU HOLD?
FOR A TIME. BUT IT'LL TAKE A MIRACLE TO SAVE US.
LEAVE THAT, GOOD CAPTAIN THOMAS, TO ME.

MAKE FOR THE DOOR, JOHN!
IF WE CAN STOP EDMUND'S MEN FROM BARRING THE KEEP...
...THIS BATTLE'S AS GOOD AS WON!

BUT EVEN AS ROBIN AND HIS BAND SURGE FORWARD...
...RESISTANCE STIFFENS.
MEN ON BOTH SIDES SELL THEIR LIVES DEARLY-- SELFLESSLY SACRIFICING THEMSELVES FOR THEIR COMRADES, PERFORMING FEATS OF EXTRAORDINARY HEROISM AND COURAGE. SUDDENLY, THE STRUGGLE'S OUTCOME-- CERTAIN MERE MOMENTS BEFORE-- SEEMS IN DOUBT.
MAY GOD DAMN DeVALERE FOR THIS!
THAT HIS AMBITION MUST LEAD SUCH MEN AS THESE TO THE SLAUGHTER!
WHAT A MAN HE MUST BE, THOUGH, TO INSPIRE SUCH LOYALTY AND DEVOTION.
COULD KING RICHARD OR PRINCE JOHN-- OR EVEN DEAD HENRY-- DO THE SAME?!

I'M LATE!
IN PART, BECAUSE I WAS-- I AM-- AFRAID.
TO FACE ELLIANNE--
--BUT MOSTLY, TO FACE EDMUND. Ahhh, CHRIST, WAS EVERY MOMENT OF OUR FRIENDSHIP A LIE, THEN, FROM THE VERY START?! COULD I HAVE BEEN SO BLIND, AND HE SO SUPREME A DECEIVER?!!
I WANT TO HATE HIM-- I NEED TO--
--BUT, EVEN NOW, I CANNOT.
I-- CAN!!
ELLIANNE!?!

I WILL NOT FIGHT YOU!
FINE.

I SHALL KILL YOU NONETHE-LESS.

I SHALL TEAR YOU LIMB FROM LIMB, DUNREITH, AND GRIND THE PIECES TO POWDER NEATH MY HEEL!
THUS, IN THAT SMALL WAY...

...SHALL I BE AVENGED!
LOVE SCORNED, FAITH BROKEN, TRUST BETRAYED--THERE ARE NO BETTER GOADS TO FURY.

DUNREITH'S SOLE HOPE IS TO SLAY ELLIANNE--NOTHING LESS WILL STOP HER--
--AND THAT, POOR FOOL, HE WILL NOT DO.

MY WINGS-- I CANNOT FLEE!
BUT HOW CAN I FIGHT--?!
I'VE HURT ELLI TOO MUCH ALREADY.

NO!
GODDESS, NO! THIS IS NOT HOW IT WAS TO BE!
EDMUND, WHAT HAVE YOU DONE?!

DEATH FOR THEM WAS TO COME QUICKLY...
...WITH LITTLE PAIN.

AND YET, WE ARE SO CLOSE-- TO STOP NOW, TO LEAVE THE GREAT SPELL INCOMPLETE, WILL MEAN THAT ALL THE HARDSHIP, THE SACRIFICE, THE SORROW, HAS BEEN FOR NAUGHT!
OUR LAND WILL FOREVER REMAIN UNDER THE YOKE OF ITS NORMAN CONQUERORS--OUR PEOPLE BE FOREVER SLAVES--SURELY SUCH A GOAL AS FREEDOM IS WORTH ANY PRICE-- GASP!?!

THE DRAGON!
BUT IS IT HERE TO DO DUNREITH'S BIDDING...

...OR THE BASTARD EDMUND'S?!
EDMUND'S.
PRAY, ELEANOR--TO GOD AND GODDESS BOTH, WITH ALL THINE HEART--TO AID US IN TONIGHT'S ENTERPRISE.
WE MUST WIN NOW...
"...OR NEVER."

MY MEN FIGHT WELL. THEY DO MY HEART PROUD. THERE IS NOTHING MORE I COULD ASK OF THEM...
...SAVE VICTORY.

"AND THAT IS CLEARLY NOT TO BE."

BROTHER--?!
GLENOWYN IS LOST. THE IMPREGNABLE KEEP HAS FALLEN.
BUT I SHALL NOT FALL WITH IT--

-- NOR SHALL THE CAUSE I CHAMPION.
THE OBSIDIAN BLADE-- ARE YOU MAD?! YOU CAN-NOT! IT IS NOT THE PROPER TIME!!
WOULD YOU RATHER SEE...

... THE RUINATION OF ALL OUR HOPES AND DREAMS?!
YOU MUST FIND ANOTHER WAY!
THERE IS NONE!

EDMUND-- DON'T!
THE MORE LIVES YOU TAKE WITH THAT ENCHANTED BLADE, THE MORE TAINTED AND TWISTED OUR MAGICKS WILL BECOME!
ONLY WE FOUR-- YOU, I, ELLIANNE AND DUNREITH-- WERE TO SUFFER FELL DAMNATION FOR OUR ACTS!
YOU WILL CONDEMN THE LAND!
H-AHAHH!
BLESSED LADY--?!
LIKE ALL MOTHERS, LORD EAMONN, I AM BOUND TO MY SON. HIS HURTS ARE MINE OWN.
CAN YOU NOT AID HIM?
AS MUCH AS I AM ABLE-- BUT HE WILL NOT STRIKE THE ONE HE LOVES MORE THAN LIFE ITSELF, AND THEREIN LIES HIS DOWNFALL.
THIS IS ONLY THE BEGINNING OF OUR TRIAL, ELEANOR...

"...THERE IS FAR WORSE YET TO COME."

I AM EDMUND DeVALERE--
-- EARL OF GLENOWYN AND RUNESIRE OF THE WESTERN MARCHES.
BY WHAT RIGHT DO YOU TRESPASS IN MY HOUSE AND SHED MY VASSALS' BLOOD?
HERETIC AND SORCERER--HE ADMITS IT!
WE NAME YOU TRAITOR, DOG, TO YOUR SOVEREIGN, RICHARD!
IN HIS AND QUEEN ELEANOR'S-- NAME, WE SEIZE THIS FOUL, UNHOLY PLACE...
...AND TAKE YOUR LIFE!

COME FOR ME THEN, SIR KNIGHT--

-- IF YOU DARE.
PHILLIP BEAUVAIS...

... DIES WITHOUT A SOUND-- HEART AND SOUL BLASTED INTO OBLIVION-- AS EDMUND'S DARK CRYSTAL BLADE PASSES THROUGH MAIL, FLESH AND BONE AS IF THEY DO NOT EXIST.
IT IS AS IF HE CUTS AIR.

HIGH OVERHEAD, HOWEVER, THE DRAGON SCREAMS FOR THE BOY--
-- FILLING THE SKY WITH AN EERILY HUMAN CRY OF AGONY-- AS A SLASH APPEARS ACROSS ITS BELLY AND BLOOD SPILLS FORTH TO COAT ITS EBONY SKIN.

A STEP-- A LIFE-- AT A TIME...
... EDMUND DESCENDS THE STAIRS.

EACH DEATH CREATES A NEW CUT. THE MORE HE SLAYS...
...THE MORE THE DRAGON BLEEDS...
...THE STRONGER HE BECOMES...
...THE MORE HE SLAYS--
--A CYCLE THAT WILL END ONLY WHEN THE DRAGON'S TRANSFORMATION IS COMPLETE.

IT IS THE CREATURE'S NATURE TO ECHO THE SOUL OF ITS HUMAN AVATAR-- ALREADY, IT FEELS THE DUNREITH PARTS OF ITSELF FADE AWAY, AS IF THEY HAD NEVER BEEN. WHAT REPLACES THEM IS FOUL BEYOND DESCRIPTION.
THE DRAGON REPRESENTS LIMITLESS POWER--YET ALL IT CAN DO IS BEAT THE AIR WITH ITS GREAT WINGS, AND CLAW A THE EARTH IN FUTILE, HELPLESS RAGE.

OUR ARMY'S BEING DRIVEN BACK-- SCATTERED--MORGAN, YOU ARE QUEEN OF FAERY, THERE MUST BE SOMETHING-- MERCY?!?
YOU BLEED!

I TOLD YOU, ELEANOR--
--MY SO AND I ARE BOUND.

MORE! THERE SHOULD BE MORE, I MUST HAVE MORE!!

Aha-- HOW KIND OF THE FATES TO SAVE THE BEST FOR LAST.
ROBIN HOOD, WILLIAM MARSHALL, BRIAN GRIFFON--
--WHICH OF YOU WILL FACE ME?!

COME SINGLY, TOGETHER-- TRY TO RUN AWAY, IF YOU LIKE-- IT MAKES NO DIFFERENCE. I'LL HAVE YOU, CURS, AND THE POXY BITCH-QUEENS WHO SET YOU ON ME!
THEIR AGE IS ENDED. THE LAND IS MINE-- AND SHALL REMAIN SO EVER-MORE!!
FROM THIS MOMENT--
--THE RED LORD RULES!

ON MIDSUMMER NIGHT, IN THE YEAR 1193, IN THE WEST COUNTRY OF ENGLAND...
...EVIL WALKS GLENOWYN CASTLE.

OVERHEAD, THE BLACK DRAGON-- LIVING SOUL OF THIS LAND-- WRITHES IN AGONY, BLOOD POURING FROM SCORES OF WOUNDS...
...STAINING ITS EBONY SKIN RED.
AT THE SAME TIME, THE BLOOD TRANSFORMS THE GREAT BEAST'S FUNDAMENTAL NATURE AS WELL--
--TWISTING THE DRAGON INEXORABLY FROM LIGHT TO SHADOW.

MORGAN, IS THERE NOTHING YOU CAN DO?!
NOT NOW. NOT YET. EDMUND'S POWER HAS GROWN TOO STRONG.
AT THIS POINT, I CAN NO MORE SAVE THIS REALM I LOVE...
...THAN I CAN MY SON JAMES.

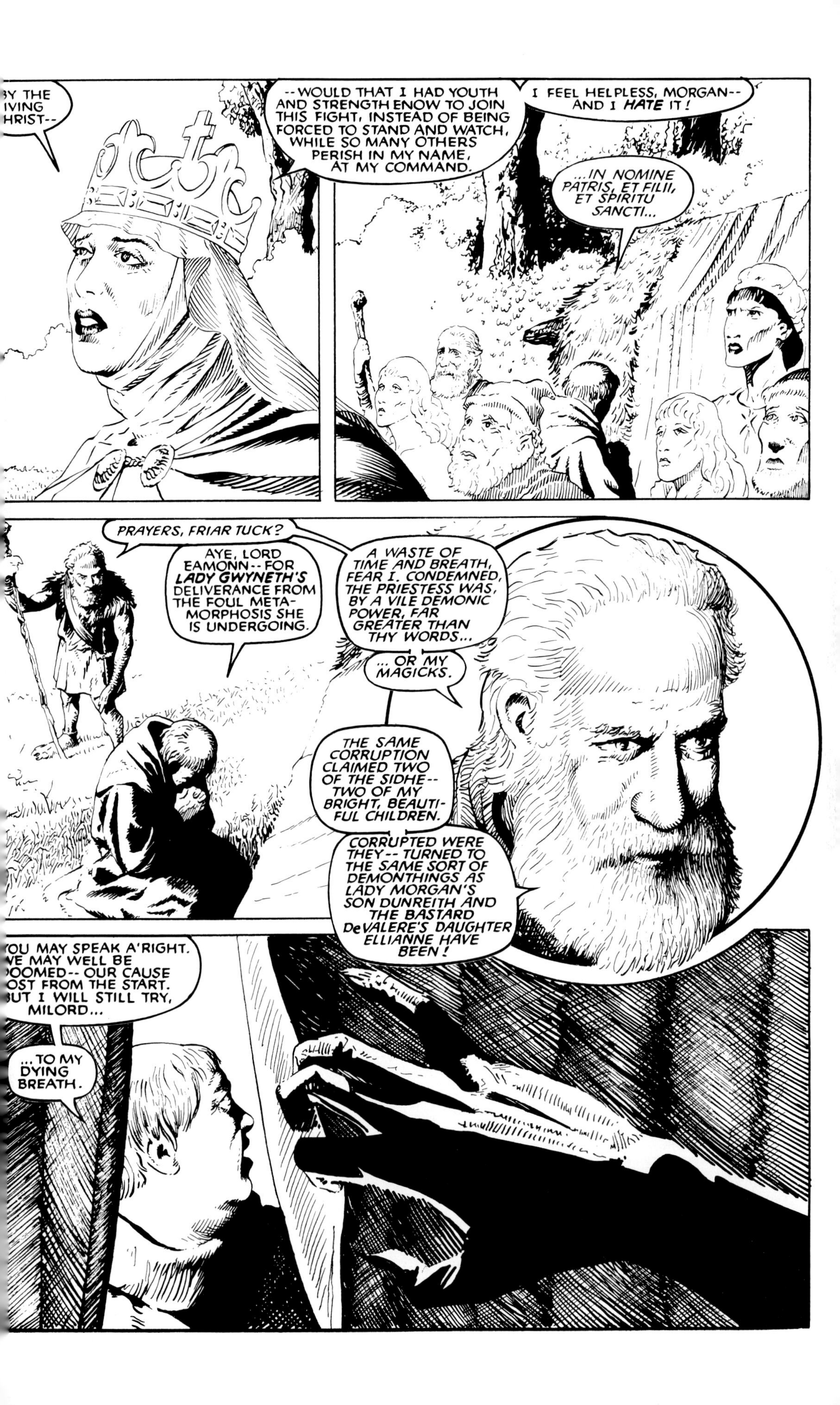

3Y THE IVING HRIST--
--WOULD THAT I HAD YOUTH AND STRENGTH ENOW TO JOIN THIS FIGHT, INSTEAD OF BEING FORCED TO STAND AND WATCH, WHILE SO MANY OTHERS PERISH IN MY NAME, AT MY COMMAND.
I FEEL HELPLESS, MORGAN-- AND I HATE IT!
...IN NOMINE PATRIS, ET FILII, ET SPIRITU SANCTI...
PRAYERS, FRIAR TUCK?
AYE, LORD EAMONN-- FOR LADY GWYNETH'S DELIVERANCE FROM THE FOUL META-MORPHOSIS SHE IS UNDERGOING.
A WASTE OF TIME AND BREATH, FEAR I. CONDEMNED, THE PRIESTESS WAS, BY A VILE DEMONIC POWER, FAR GREATER THAN THY WORDS...
... OR MY MAGICKS.
THE SAME CORRUPTION CLAIMED TWO OF THE SIDHE-- TWO OF MY BRIGHT, BEAUTIFUL CHILDREN.
CORRUPTED WERE THEY-- TURNED TO THE SAME SORT OF DEMONTHINGS AS LADY MORGAN'S SON DUNREITH AND THE BASTARD DeVALERE'S DAUGHTER ELLIANNE HAVE BEEN!
OU MAY SPEAK A'RIGHT. VE MAY WELL BE OOMED-- OUR CAUSE OST FROM THE START. UT I WILL STILL TRY, MILORD...
...TO MY DYING BREATH.

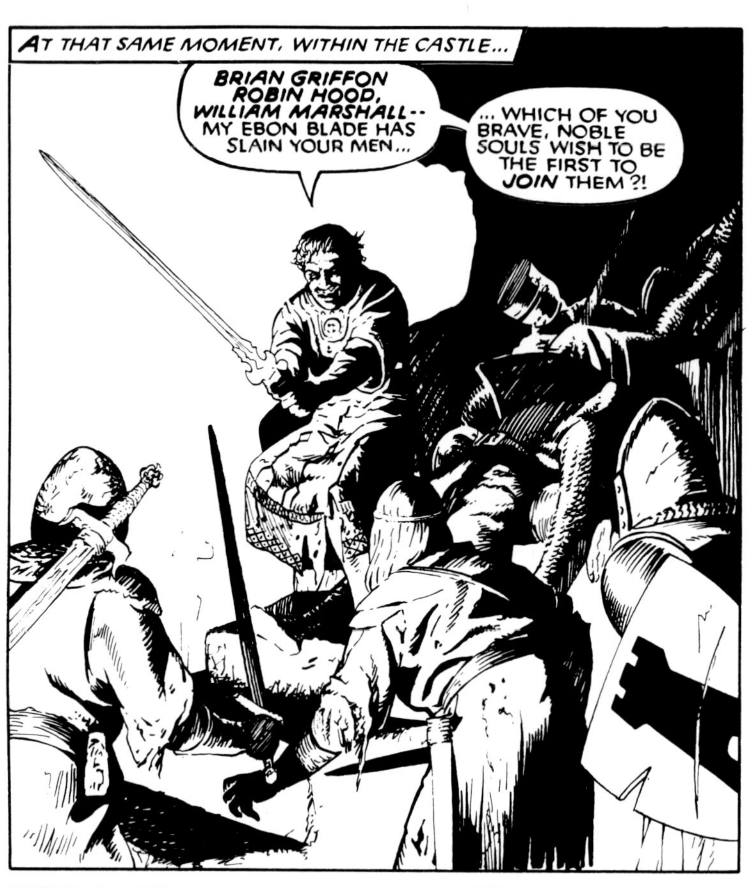
AT THAT SAME MOMENT, WITHIN THE CASTLE...
BRIAN GRIFFON ROBIN HOOD, WILLIAM MARSHALL-- MY EBON BLADE HAS SLAIN YOUR MEN...
...WHICH OF YOU BRAVE, NOBLE SOULS WISH TO BE THE FIRST TO JOIN THEM?!

FOLLOW ME, MEN OF GLENOWYN!
OUR LIVES, OUR BLOOD, TO SAVE EARL EDMUND'S!

THEY'RE DRIVING US BACK!
LET 'EM, WOLFSHEAD!
WE'VE NO DEFENSE AGAINST DeVALERE AND HIS ACCURSED SWORD!

FOOLS! TRAITORS!!
YOU DARE DEPRIVE ME OF MY RIGHTFUL PREY?!
B-BUT, MY LORD EARL-- WE SOUGHT TO SAVE YOU!

EDMUND--BROTHER-- I BEG YOU, FORBEAR!
THE DRAGON IS YOURS, TH BATTLE WON! LET NO MORE FALL TONIGHT, SAVE THOSE WHO WILL BE CLAIMED BY OUR GRAND ENCHANTMENT
SHEATHE YOUR SWORD-- SHOW MERCY!
IT'S TOO LATE FOR THAT

'LL NOT QUIT SO LONG AS A SINGLE OE STANDS! THEIR EVERY LIFE ND SOUL IS FORFEIT!
LL MY DAYS, ANNE, 'VE ENDURED THE NEERS AND INSULTS ND CURSES OF LESSER MEN-- MY FRIENDSHIP WAS EVER RETURNED...
... WITH CONTEMPT OR OUT-RIGHT HATRED!

TONIGHT, AT LAST, EDMUND DeVALERE-- THE BASTARD HALFBREED-- GIVES AS GOOD AS HE GOT!

DARK LADY, FORGIVE ME! I NEVER DREAMED--!
WHAT MADNESS HAVE I UNLEASHED UPON THE WORLD--
GASP?!

I LOVED YOU, JAMES DUNREITH-- WITH ALL MY HEART!
BUT YOU REPAID ME WITH AGONY BEYOND COMPREHENSION. YOU STRIPPED ME OF MY HUMANITY! ALL I AM-- ALL I DO-- IS BECAUSE OF YOU!
AS YOU CAST ME FOREVER INTO THE ABYSS...

...SO I NOW HURL YOU INTO THE FLAMES!

BROTHER--?! THOSE ARE YOUR LOYAL SOLDIERS!
THEY BLOCK MY ROAD--THEY KEEP ME FROM THE TRIUMPH I HAVE EARNED--THAT'S ALL THAT MATTERS!
M'LORD--
YGAAIEAIEE!

HELP ROB ACROSS THE DRAWBRIDGE, WILLIAM MARSHALL! I'LL COVER YOU!
DeVALERE'S GONE BERSERK, BRIAN!
SLAUGHTERING HIS OWN--HE DOESN'T KNOW WHAT HE'S DOING!

Ah, ROB--IF ONLY THA' WERE TRUE.
AT LEAST YOU TWO ARE SAFE--TO FIGHT ANOTHER DAY.
THIS IS AS IT SHOULD BE.

THE GRIFFON, STANDING FOR--AND AGAINST--THE DRAGON. ALONE!

BRIAN--?!!
HE'S DROPPED THE PORTCULLIS!

THE FOOL SCOTSMAN--HASN'T HE LEARNED, TO FACE DeVALERE IS SUICIDE!
I WONDER. WE FOUGHT WITH STEEL--
--BUT, LOOK YOU, MILORD! THAT'S THE SACRED DUNREITH BLADE GRIFFON WIELDS! IT'S FAERY-FORGED--ELDRITCH CRYSTAL BONDED WITH SILVER. IF ANY WEAPON'S A MATCH FOR THE BASTARD'S DEMON BLADE, IT'S THAT.

UT WHAT
F THE MAN--
S HE EQUAL
O THE TASK?!
IF ONLY I HAD AN ARROW AND MY BOW!

DREAM ON, LOCKSLEY.
WHILE JAMES DUNREITH WAS HUMAN, HE WAS THE DRAGON'S HUMAN AVATAR, BUT NOW THE GREAT BEAST IS NEARLY WHOLLY EDMUND'S. WITH ITS POWER IN HIS HANDS...
...DeVALERE CAN RESHAPE THE WORLD!

YOU'RE A POOR SUBSTITUTE FOR YOUR MASTER, VILLEIN...

WHOUNFFF!
...WITH MORE COURAGE THAN SKILL.

YOU'LL PROVE A MOMENTARY DISTRACTION, NOTHING MORE.

LESSED
IRGIN
OTHER--?!!
LADY GWYNETH-- HER TRANSFORMATION'S COMPLETE!
I AM SUMMONED!
MY DREAD MASTER, I MUST SERVE!
ROYAL BLOOD I MUST SHED! AND ON ROYAL FLESH, FEAST!

SLAY THE MONSTER!
NO!
GWYNETH TREHERNE IS AN INNOCENT! SHE IS TO BE TAKEN ALIVE AND UNHARMED!
BE PRACTICAL, MAJESTY!
CONTAGIOUS IS HER DEMON TAINT! IF SHE DRAWS HUMAN OR FAERY BLOOD, THAT PERSON WILL BE TRANS-FORMED THE SAME AS SHE!
NEVERTHELESS, EAMONN, SUCH IS MY COMMAND.
YOU'RE BEATEN, SCOT. YOU'VE NOWHERE LEFT TO RUN!
BUT I'M A GENEROUS MAN. I OFFER A CHOICE OF FATES -- YOU CAN FOLLOW YOUR MASTER INTO THE FLAMES.
OR BE SLAIN BY MY BLADE -- WHICH MEANS YOUR OWN NOT INCONSIDER-ABLE ARCANE MIGHT WILL BE ADDED TO THAT ALREADY USED BY ME TO ENCHAIN THE DRAGON!
OR YOU CAN BE SCARRED BY ELLIANNE, REMADE IN HER IMAGE --
-- TO TAKE DUNREITH'S PLACE AS HER CONSORT.

TOP IT! TOP IT!! STOP IT!!!
I'LL BEAR NO MORE OF THIS! EDMUND, YOU'RE SLAYING THE VERY PEOPLE WE SOUGHT TO FREE AND SAVE!

THEIR LIVES ARE NOTHING! A NECESSARY SACRIFICE!
THE PLAN IS ALL, THE DREAM IS ALL!

NOT AT SUCH A PRICE!
THE LORDS AND LADIES OF YOUR TABLE-- BY THEIR OWN ACTIONS-- CHOSE THEIR DOOM! THESE POOR, INNOCENT SOULS DESERVE BETTER!
THEY HAVE DEFIED THEIR LIEGE! THEY WILL LEARN THEIR LESSON--

--AS SHALL YOU!

LADY--
--ANNE!?!

I BURN--
--AS IF THE BLADE HAD CUT ME?!!

SHE YET LIVES!

BUT-- EVERYONE ELSE PERISHED WITH THE CRYSTAL'S MEREST TOUCH!
THEY... WERE HUMAN, MY CHILD. YOU AND I...
... ARE SOMETHING MORE.

MY HAND--?!!

AT LAST, BITCH, YOUR TRUE COLORS ARE REVEALED!
BUT I'LL NOT PERMIT YOU TO BETRAY ME!

BRAVE TALK, EDMUND--
-- FROM ONE WHO'S BETRAYED EVERY PROMISE, EVERY OATH...
... EVERY FRIEND!

THAT RING-- THE DUNREITH SIGNET!
JAMIE GAVE IT ME AS A PLEDGE OF OUR LOVE...
... OUR ETERNAL DEVOTION.
WHAT IS HAPPENIN TO ME?! LAD ANNE, WHA HAVE YOU DONE?!

"REVEALED THE... TRUTH...
"... OF WHO AND WHAT... YOU ARE...
"... MY DEAREST...
"... DAUGHTER.
YOU-- MY MOTHER?!
YOU?!?
IT CANNOT BE! YOU AND MY FATHER ARE BROTHER AND SISTER! THAT MEANS I-- I--!!
NO!
HAT WAS A CRUEL DECEPTION. YOUR TRUE SIRE AS ONE OF THE ANCIENT BLOOD, A PRINCE OF AERY-- AS YOUR VISAGE NOW REVEALS.
LOVED HIM, ELLIANNE, AS DO YOU-- BUT I SLEW HIM ONETHELESS, FOR WHAT I ELIEVED WAS A GREATER OOD. I WAS PREPARED TO O THE SAME WITH YOU, TO AY ANY PRICE TO FREE OUR AND FROM NORMAN TYRANNY O RESTORE THE OLD WAYS O THEIR PROPER, PRE-EMINENT PLACE.
I WAS A FOOL!

FORGIVE ME, ELLIANNE. I THOUGHT YOUR SACRIFICE NECESSARY. A SMALL WRONG TO BRING ABOUT A HAPPY END. I SHOULD HAVE KNOWN BETTER.
I NEVER IMAGINED YOUR UNCLE COULD BE SO MAD--SO CONSUMED WITH HATRED.
YOU MUST BELIEVE-- IN THE BEGINNING, OUR DREAM SEEMED SO NOBLE, SO RIGHT. I-- WE-- NEVER INTENDED TO CREATE SUCH... EVIL.
Ohhh, ELLI-- THINK NOT TOO ILL OF ME...
...WHO LEARNED TOO LATE THAT I WOULD RATHER PERISH...
...THAN SEE A DREAM, PERVERTED INTO FOULEST NIGHTMARE...
...CLAIM MY CHILD...
YOU'RE DONE, GRIFFON!
LORD EDMUND--
--FATHER--
--NO!
SHE'LL NO SAVE YOU DOG!
THIS LIFE, ABOVE ALL...
...I'LL NOT BE CHEATED OF!

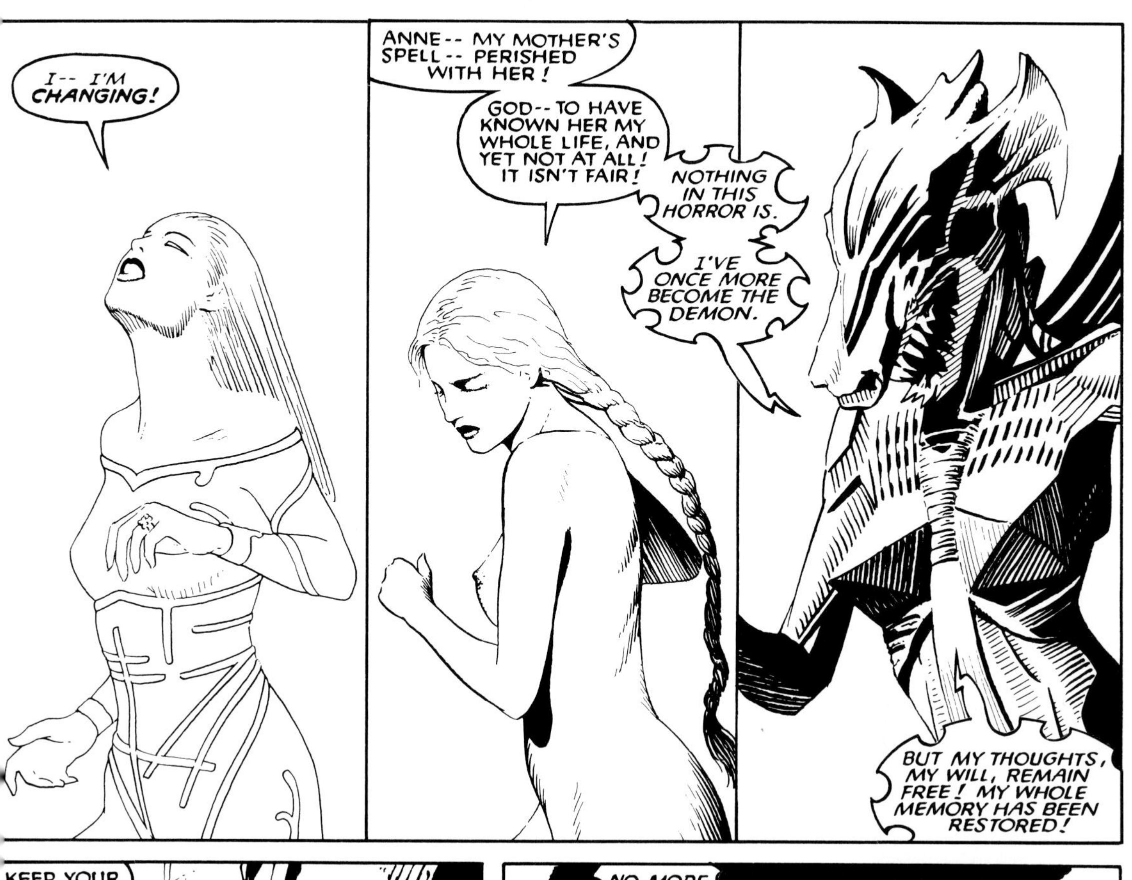
I-- I'M CHANGING!
ANNE-- MY MOTHER'S SPELL-- PERISHED WITH HER!
GOD-- TO HAVE KNOWN HER MY WHOLE LIFE, AND YET NOT AT ALL! IT ISN'T FAIR!
NOTHING IN THIS HORROR IS.
I'VE ONCE MORE BECOME THE DEMON.
BUT MY THOUGHTS, MY WILL, REMAIN FREE! MY WHOLE MEMORY HAS BEEN RESTORED!

KEEP YOUR DISTANCE, GIRL!
DIE NOW OR LATER, IS THERE A DIFFERENCE?
I LOVED YOU AS MY FATHER, EDMUND.
WAS YOUR LOVE FOR ME...
... A LIE?

NO MORE, NO LESS--
-- THAN THE LOVE HE PROFESSED FOR ME!

JAMIE!?!
I'M SORRY, ELLI--
I HURT YOU SO.
ALL WE HAD-- ALL WE COULD HAVE BEEN--
--IT'S GONE FOREVER.
NAUGHT REMAINS BUT SCARS, AND ASHES.
-- FOR WHAT WAS, WHAT IS...
...WHAT MUST NOW BE.
HOW HEROIC A POSE, JAMIE.
HOW NOBLE A GESTURE.
AND HOW FUTILE!
YOU SEE, I MEAN TO WIN-- I CARE NOT HOW!
DRAGON-- HEAR AND HEED THY LORD!
ROUT THE RABBLE OPPOSING ME AND, MOST ESPECIALLY, SLAY THE MAJESTIES OF ENGLAND AND FAERY!!
TOO MANY HAVE SUFFERED AT YOUR HANDS, EDMUND!
LET YOUR LIFE-- AND OURS-- BE THE LAST TO FALL.
AYE, ELLI-- SAVE THEM, IF YOU CAN.

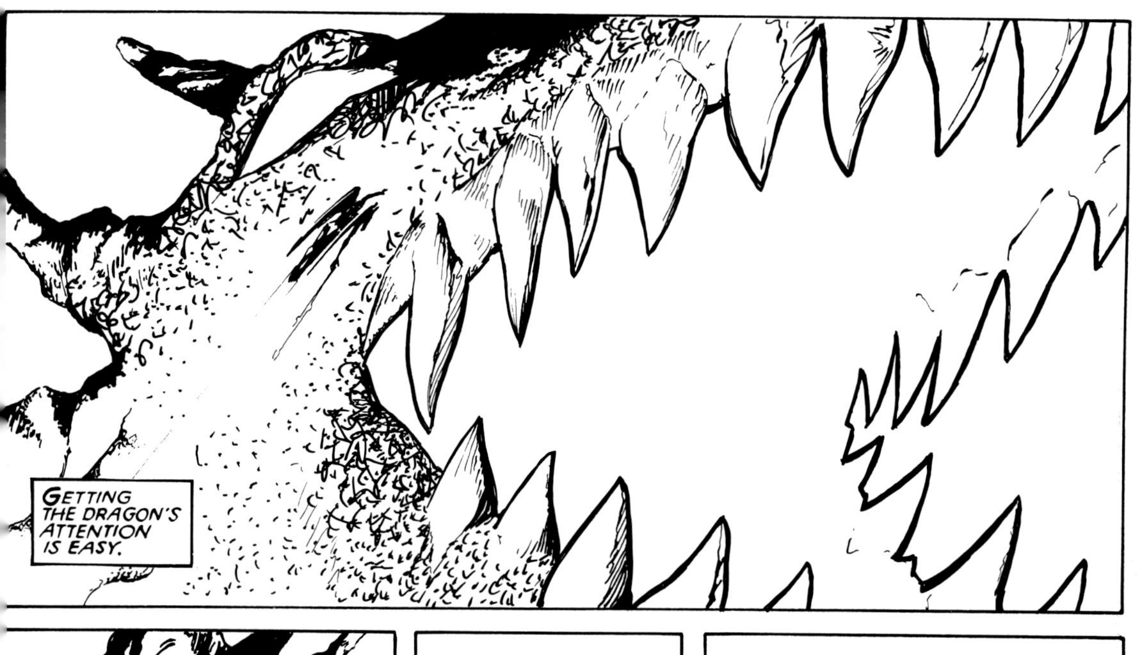
GETTING THE DRAGON'S ATTENTION IS EASY.

SURVIVING IS LESS SO.

ON EVERY FRONT, EDMUND'S FORCES TAKE A DEADLY TOLL.
HIS TRIUMPH SEEMS MORE AND MORE ASSURED.
MORGAN-- WHEN FIRST SHE APPEARED SHE FLOATED IN THE AIR, SHE WAS NOT WHOLLY OF THIS WAKING WORLD.
BUT NOW, SHE STANDS UPON THE GROUND. AND SEEMS ALMOST... HUMAN.
THE FORCES OF LIGHT ARE FADING. EDMUND'S SHADOW DARKENS BOTH THE LAND AND THE SOULS OF ALL WHO DWELL IN IT.
WOLFSHEAD-- RALLY YOUR OUTLAWS!
THE QUEEN'S IN DANGER!
AYE, LET'S GO.
WE'RE OF PRECIOUS LITTLE USE HERE.
I ALWAYS KNEW THIS IS THE WAY WE TWO WOULD END.
WHY?!
DAMN YOU, EDMUND-- WHY?!!
YOU WERE A MAN OF HONOR-- I WAS YOUR FRIEND-- HOW COULD YOU HAVE DONE THIS?!
THE LAND MUST BE FREE. I MUST BE ITS LIBERATOR!
YOU-- THE ANOINTED ONE -- SHIRKED YOUR RESPONSIBILITY. YOU ABANDONED YOUR HERITAGE, YOU LET HENRY PLANTAGENET SEND YOU INTO EXILE WHEN YOU COULD HAVE STAYED AND FOUGHT!
YOU COULD HAVE LED A REBELLION THEN, SHOULD HAVE, I'D HAVE GLADLY, LAUGHINGLY, JOINED YOU!
BUT YOU FAILED THAT TRUE TEST. YOU FLED!
I KEPT SILENT AND STAYED AT THE COURT. I TOOK YOUR PLACE!

YOU FORFEITED YOUR RIGHT TO CLAIM THE DRAGON, JAMIE!

YOU LACK THE STRENGTH OF BODY AND WILL TO BE ITS MASTER!

ONLY I -- THE BASTARD HALFBREED-- PART HUMAN, PART FAERY, PART NORMAN-- A PART OF NOTHING, APART FROM ALL--!

ONLY I AM TRULY WORTHY!
MY SON!
AS THY LIFE EBBS...
...SO DOES MINE.
AND WITH MY STRENGTH, FADES THINE.
THE DRAGON... BELONGS TO EDMUND. ITS METAMORPHOSIS IS COMPLETE.
WITH JAMIE'S DEATH DeVALERE'S SPELL WILL STRIKE DOWN EVERY MAN, WOMAN AND CHILD IN THIS REALM, ELEANOR, WITH EVEN A DROP OF NORMAN BLOOD IN THEIR VEINS- A SLAUGHTER THAT WILL TAINT THE LAND 'TIL TIME'S END!

I SAID, NO MORE WILL SUFFER, AND NONE PERISH THIS NIGHT--
-- SAVE THOSE WHO DESERVE IT!

AND BY THE PIT MY FALSE FATHER HAS MADE MY HOME...
...I'LL NOT BE FORSWORN!

THINK, JAMIE, OF THE PRICE OF VICTORY.
SLAY ME-- AND YOU LIVE.
TO REMEMBER ALL YOU'VE DONE.
MINE WAS THE VOICE THAT GAVE THE ORDERS--

--YOURS THE CLAWS THAT KILLED AND MAIMED AND RAVISHED!
CAN YOU ENDURE SUCH TORMENT?

I OFFER SWEET OBLIVION.

"NONE WILL FORGET."
THY MAN, DUNREITH, DID THIS! WHY DOTH THOU AID HIM?!

"NONE FORGIVE."
THOU WAST HURT AS DEEP AS I!
THOU SHOULDST HELP ME TEAR THE RAVISHER TO SHREDS!
JAMIE IS AS MUCH A VICTIM AS WE, GWYNETH! IT IS EDMUND WHO'S TO BLAME!

LIAR-- YAEEAIII!
MERCIFUL LADY!

THE MAIN WALL'S GONE-- WHAT A MESS!
JAMIE'S IN THE CENTRAL KEEP, WITH DeVALERE!

I'D BEST JOIN --
eh?!!
BRIAN--!
MASTER GRIFFON--!?!
Och, LASS!

YET... ANOTHER CURSE OF THIS FORM --
--TO BE BROKEN, WELL NIGH TO BITS, YET NEVER, IT SEEMS, TO DIE.

Oh, ELLIANNE--!?!
LORD GOD-- COULD YOU NOT HAVE CLAIMED ME SOONER, AND SPARED ME THIS AWFUL MOMENT!

DO NOT TOUCH... MAJESTY!
MY FLESH... SO SHARP-- IT WILL SURELY CUT YOU!
I HAVE SEEN BLOOD-- AND SHED MY SHARE--
--AND SHALL NO DOUBT ENDURE FAR WORSE BEFORE I'M FINISHED.
HUSH NOW, CHILD --LET US SAVE YOU...

... IF WE CAN.
THERE IS A WAY. BECAUSE THE DEMONS ARE TWINNED IN FORM AND NATURE, I CAN CAST THE LIFE-FORCE OF ONE INTO THE BODY OF THE OTHER. THE SURVIVOR WILL BE OUR CHAMPION, THE REALM'S LAST HOPE.
THOU, ELLIANNE, MUST NEEDS CHOOSE.
WHO SHALL BE SACRIFICED?

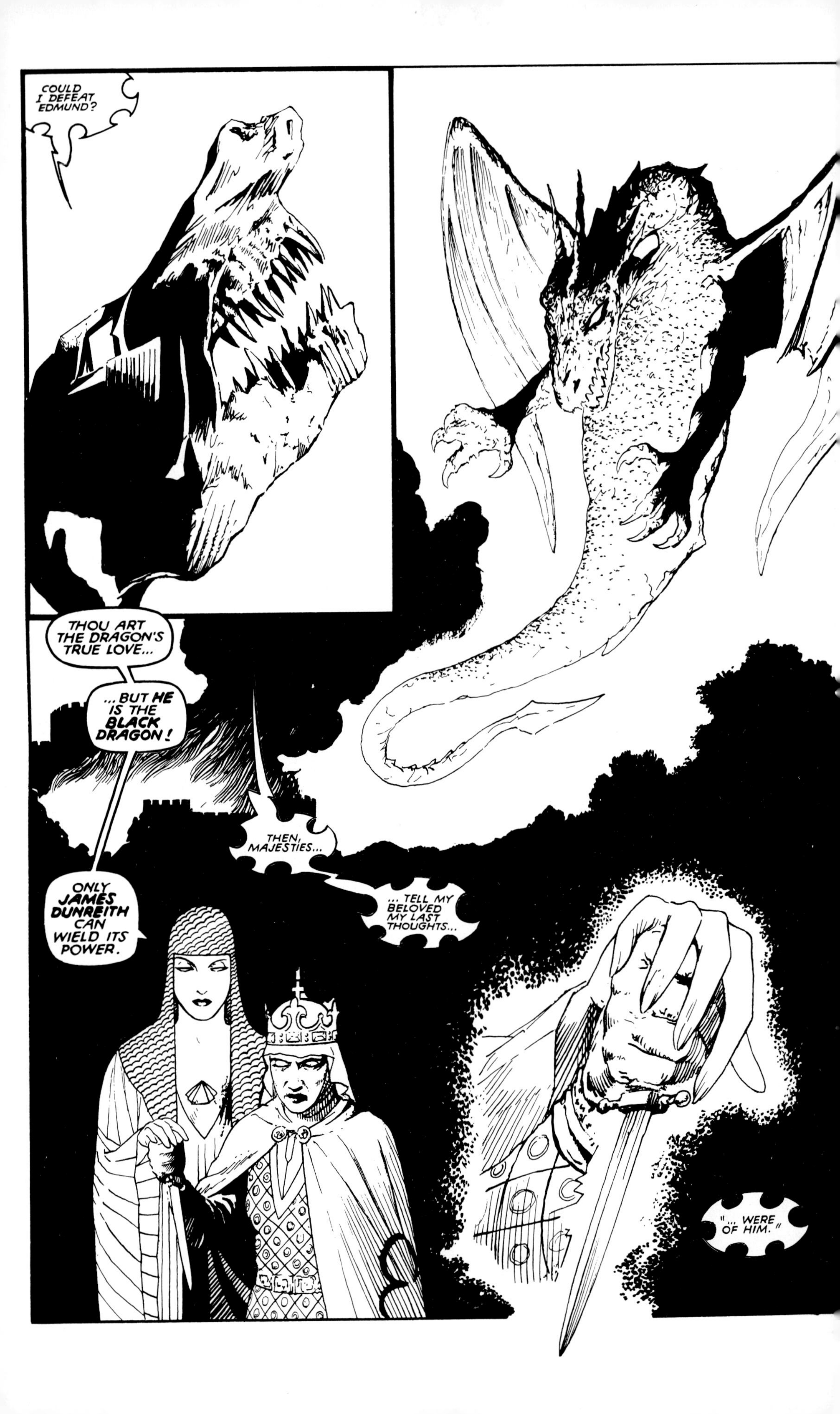
COULD I DEFEAT EDMUND?
THOU ART THE DRAGON'S TRUE LOVE...
...BUT HE IS THE BLACK DRAGON!
ONLY JAMES DUNREITH CAN WIELD ITS POWER.
THEN, MAJESTIES...
...TELL MY BELOVED MY LAST THOUGHTS...
"...WERE OF HIM."

ELLIANNE!

YOU SPEAK OF WORTH, EDMUND!
OF COWARDICE! OF DISHONOR!
OF INJURIES TOO LONG UNAVENGED!

BUT MINE ARE NO LESS THAN YOURS!
A NORMAN SLEW MY FATHER! A NORMAN NAMED DeVALERE!

I, TOO, HAD CAUSE TO HATE!
BUT I FOUND A BETTER ROAD!

GRIFFON, STAND THINE ARMY WELL AWAY FROM GLENOWYN.
IT IS NO LONGER SAFE FOR MAN OR FAERY-FOLK.
GO'ST THOU WITH HIM, ELEANOR, I PRAY THEE. THY WORK IS DONE. WHAT REMAINS IS FOR ME ALONE.
MAKE HASTE-- THOU HAST PRECIOUS LITTLE TIME.
YOU LET YOUR HATRED FESTER WITHIN YOU, EDMUND, LIKE A LEPROSY OF THE SPIRIT!
HOW EASILY YOU CONDEMN!
ALL THE BEST GIFTS OF HUMAN AND FAERY HERITAGE WERE YOURS.
I DESERVED THE SAME-- I SHOULD HAVE BEEN AS BLESSED AS YOU--
--YET I WAS GIVEN NOTHING!

YES, I RAGED! I HAD GOOD REASON!
TO HAVE RANK AND POSITION-- KNOWING IT COULD BE STRIPPED FROM ME AT ANY TIME, REGARDLESS OF MY SERVICE AND DEVOTION! TO BE OF FAERY-- KNOWING MINE WAS A MORTAL FORM, BUT WITH A SPAN MORTAL!
TO LOVE YOU-- KNOWING IT WOULD NEVER BE RETURNED!
I GRIEVE FOR YOU, MY FRIEND.